PSYCHOKINESIOLOGY

Doorway
to the
Unconscious
Mind

ALEXANDER S. HOLUB, Ph.D.

With

Evelyn Budd-Michaels, Ph.d.

For permissions, or serializations, condensations, adaptations, or for our catalog of other publications, write the Publisher at the address below.

Library of Congress Cataloging-in-Publication Data

Holub, Alexander S. (Alexander Stephen), 1943
Psychokinesiology: Doorway to The Unconscious Mind / by
Alexander Holub with Evelyn Budd-Michaels

p. cm.
Includes bibliographic references and index
ISBN 1-893157-06-7

1. Mind and body therapies. 2. Applied Kinesiology —
Psychological aspects. Psychology, Human Behavior. I. Michaels,
Evelyn B. (Evelyn Budd), 1930-

II. Title.
RC489.M53H65 1999
616.89'1--dc21   99-38726
                                                                                      CIP

Published by
BRIDGER HOUSE PUBLISHERS, INC
P.O. Box 2208, Carson City, NV 89702, 1-800-729-4131

Cover design by The Right Type
Printed in the United States of America
10 9 8 7 6 5 4 3 2 1

Acknowledgements

*Thanks to my model, Alexandra Mahlke
and to Sherry Holub for the photography.*

*Special thanks to Evelyn Budd-Michaels for
introducing me to Applied Kinesiology
and for being my partner as we
developed, and continue to develop
this system for personal change.*

*A special thanks also goes to Dr. Victor Frank, D.C. the developer of
Total Body Modification (TBM) and Dr. Allan Phillips, D.C.
the developer of NeuroLink 2000 both of whom knew about the
work that I am doing and allowed me to join in their class programs
knowing that I was going to liberally borrow from their techniques.*

TABLE OF CONTENTS

INTRODUCTION

Take a walk down any street in any town or city and look at the people there. How many are truly walking proudly (not arrogantly) with a vibrancy and rhythm in each step concerned and caring about themselves, their accomplishments and about others? Most people are not aware of what is going on around them nor do they appear happy. Often, the only way they feel that they can handle emotional situations effectively is to overreact. In overreacting they feel they have some semblance of control. Many of them appear to be simply existing from day to day trudging along as if they have the weight of the world on their shoulders. If you could get into their thinking processes you will most likely find that the vast majority of people assume that they have few, if any, choices. They see themselves as victims of their past, of their emotions, of the whims of the universe, and of other people's actions and choices. Life holds no joy for them and they are dissatisfied with what they consider to be their "lot in life."

If you see an animal that is plodding along holding its head as if it is a struggle to keep it up moving as if it has no awareness of its environment you will immediately think that there must be something wrong with it. If you see the average person on a street carrying himself in a manner similar to that animal you usually do not concern yourself with him. You do not want to get involved. Frequently you will consider this as relatively normal for that person and go on your way. Actually, this is not normal for any human being.

If, on the other hand, you see someone who is full of life, acting happily and walking and greeting everyone as if (s)he is glad to be alive you will probably stop and stare because this does not happen very often. Many times you will hear the comment that there must be something wrong with someone who has a zest for life. This condition, in actuality, is what is more normal for human beings.

It is not normal to plod along slumping as you go. It is also not normal to be unaware of the world around you leading a joyless life filled with emotionally trying situations and emotional overreactions. It is true that stress is a natural part of life but this does not mean that overreacting to stressful situations is the best way to deal with stress. There is ample evidence that emotions are a major contributing factor to many physiological disorders such as heart problems, ulcers, arthritis and even cancer. Many researchers who have observed cultures where there is an extremely low incidence of many of these diseases have noticed that in these cultures the emotional responses to life's situations tend to be more *appropriate* to the situation. In fact, many of the members of the long-lived societies throughout the world have a more relaxed, "go with the flow" attitude toward what may happen in life. They never hold on to their emotions releasing them quickly.

Many people think that the "go with the flow" attitude means nothing more than not caring about anything; to be unconcerned no matter what happens to oneself or to anyone else. This is unrealistic. What needs to be done is to define "go with the flow." The simplest meaning of this term is *acceptance*. Not to the point of egocentricism or a lack of caring but an unconditional appreciation for the learning involved in every situation and an appreciation for oneself and others.

To many, adopting the "go with the flow" attitude of acceptance appears to be nothing less than a immense struggle. To these people it means that they must attach themselves to someone who has set themselves up as an authority of some sort, to attach themselves to a group or to become someone else. Never does this give them peace. Many fear making change because it appears that there is a loss of control and the predictability of their world immediately disappears. There is a belief in the western world that if you do not constantly exert control over things and people then you would be under the control of someone or something else. Invariably there are both relationship and health problems because of this attitude.

As a therapist you generally deal with people who notice that they have a problem and want to change. One of the most frustrating experiences that any therapist can have is being unable to get the desired results with a particular client. The client has the knowledge, the skills, the desire, and the motivation but something does not seem to be happening. Often, the more aware client will also notice that (s)he is not having the progress in the areas that are desired and this can increase your feelings of frustration. So, in order to better assist your client you may have even begun searching and looking for more techniques for your arsenal for change. Then, as you began applying the new techniques something still seemed to be missing. Many of the traditional therapeutic and counseling techniques are quite good. They are able get an understanding of many of the basics for a problematic behavior. They just do not get deeply enough into the unconscious beginnings and motivators of that problematic behavior. Consequently, their full effect is limited.

If you are like many therapists you have probably wished that you had a "magic wand" or some sort of reliable method that can get beyond the conscious and unconscious blocks. Imagine if you were able to circumvent a client's defenses and get to the root of a problematic behavior in minutes instead of weeks, months, or even years. Think of being able to have your client confront the roots of the problems with little or no catharsis; even though many therapies view emotional catharsis as a positive sign. It would certainly be considered next to a miracle if the problem behavior, attitude, belief or emotion is readjusted quickly and easily and other personal resources brought into play. This would make coping with life much easier. This, you have most likely thought, is not possible. Or is it?

Psychologically, there are three main motivating features to human conduct: thoughts, feelings, and behaviors. All three are interconnected and interrelated. This interconnection is a closed feedback-loop where thoughts, feelings, and behaviors constantly reinforce one another. You behave the way that you do because of your thoughts and feelings toward a specific thing, event or person. In turn, those thoughts and feelings motivate you to behave in specific ways toward those particular things, events or persons. What is important to remember is that many of your thoughts, feelings and behaviors toward a thing, event or person were learned. You continue to act on them because they are embedded in your nervous system and have become part of you. These consistent behaviors are, in fact, part of what you have accepted as your identification. This does not mean that they cannot be changed. Since it is a feedback loop, by changing one part of the process, the others will naturally change. If you have consistently acted one particular way in a situation, once you have changed your perspective on it you will find yourself acting differently when confronted by that or any similar situation. Traditional therapies concern themselves with changing your perspective by finding other ways of dealing with those troubling situations. This is done either by directly changing your thinking or feelings, or by changing the rewarding aspects of the situation (behavior modification). In this way there is a conscious effort toward making that change. There is nothing wrong with a concerted effort to make changes. Once you have made the change you will come away with a good feeling of accomplishment and a better self-image.

This is all well and good. The only problem is that it can take a lot of time to get to the actual disturbance and even more time dealing with it. Most therapies fail to recognize that there is a difference between the *Time of Awareness* of a problem and the *Time of Origin*. Traditional talking therapies tend to go back as far as the *Time of Awareness*. Quite often the *Time of Origin* is totally out of awareness because it may be *in utero* or be a *genetic predisposition*. This is what makes it difficult to access.

There is a large amount of data available which deals with problems encountered while in utero. It is a fact that whatever emotions the mother feels, the fetus feels as well. So, if the mother is having a stressful experience the biochemicals that are flowing through the mother's bloodstream go through the umbilical cord into the fetus. The fetus will have a stressful experience at the same time. The difference is that the fetus has no idea what is causing the experience of stress. It can only associate the mother's bodily shifts and muffled sounds that it may be hearing as being the possible causes of the stress. After the child is born then other associations are made. When the child hears sounds which may be similar to those encountered in utero (due to generalization) stressful biochemicals will result and a situation which may have no real stress in itself can become stressful through unconscious associations. The fact remains that it is quite likely that the external situation that the child is experiencing has nothing to do with the experience that the mother had gone through and which affected the fetus in utero. With this description you can also get the idea of the difference between the *Time of Awareness* of a problem and its *Time of Origin*.

In the twenty or so years of twin studies it has been found that there is a 50-50 relationship between heredity and environment. That is, 50 percent of your behaviors, attitudes, and personality traits are learned and 50 percent are inherited. Much of what is inherited are *predispositions* to behaviors, attitudes, and personality traits. Although there are some personality traits which are inherited, it is the environment which triggers the predispositions into behavioral patterns. Once the predisposition is initially triggered we have the ***Time of Awareness*** of a problem. The ***Time of Origin*** is always some time prior to the environmental trigger. So, going back to the *Time of Origin* can be quite difficult. A problem that had occurred in utero is difficult enough to get to. One that is genetically inherited is impossible through traditional methods. An interesting point: Genetic inheritance may be the explanation for what some therapists have encountered as descriptions of physical and sexual abuse in a client's childhood where there is literally no proof of it ever occurring. Exploring this, without attempting to get the client to believe in its validity, may be a way of accessing the *Time of Origin* of a problem. The best way to look at this sort of situation is symbolic and representational of something underlying the conflict. It is *not* the beginning of the conflict. It is simply one of the *layers* holding the conflict in place.

There is no doubt that therapy is an "after-the-fact" process. A person goes to a therapist only *after* the behavior, attitudes, and so on have gotten into his/her way of dealing effectively with life. Then both the client and therapist get together on a program that is hoped will affect the client's life in positive ways. In traditional Freudian psychoanalysis free association is used. With it the patient talks about anything that comes to mind in the session. It is hoped that during these unstructured sessions that sooner or later the patient will hit on the cause of the problem. This process is slow and can take years of almost daily sessions. Gestalt therapy considers the different "parts" of the client as well as how (s)he emotionally deals with life's situations. You can expect generally from five to ten years in this therapeutic process. In the cognitive techniques the client's thinking processes are confronted and the irrational and illogical reasoning behind these thoughts is disputed immediately. In this process the client is taught how to take control of his/her thinking and consequential emotional responding. This can take anywhere from several months to two or three years depending on the individual. It is obvious that the cognitive techniques are much more efficient and there appears to be ample research to show that they tend to be quite effective as well. The only problem with the cognitive techniques is that it takes a certain type of individual to work most effectively with them.

It does not matter what techniques that the therapist may use, talking therapy has its drawbacks. One of the main drawbacks is that of the client's conscious thinking processes. Conscious thinking tends to get in the way of any effective intervention by selecting the emotions and experiences that it wants to have come up from the unconscious. Consequently, it is necessary to get beyond these conscious processes. Once beyond the conscious rationalizations the unconscious operations will be more open to investigation. Consequently, the most elegant[1] method for getting through and beyond the conscious thinking processes will affect the client in the most positive way causing the greatest change. Effective change, though, is a difficult thing to define. To many psychologists a client has changed only when (s)he is acting somewhat differently than before. A behavioral change implies that something in the thinking processes has shifted. Often change is based on the reward system that the client has in his/her environment. The first law of behavioristic psychology is: "Whatever you reinforce, you will get more of." What this means is that you will continue performing a particular behavior as long as you will be getting, or even expecting to get, a reward for it or from it. So, change can be nothing more than looking at your reward system and altering that in some way. That is not an effective way of dealing with many problematic behaviors. As any parent knows, if you do not find other ways of dealing with a child's unwanted behaviors, simply not rewarding, or even punishing, a specific behavior can bring out something else that could be worse. Getting to the *Time of Origin* of the problem and dealing with it from that point can shift it from a stressful experience to a learning experience.

One thing that human beings are great at doing is making generalizations. A generalization is assigning to a class of similar persons, objects, or events the same (or a very similar) response. Generalization has both good and bad points. First of all, it makes the world much more predictable and easier to handle. This predictability helps to sort through and classify the things that happen to us every day. Second, generalizations can attribute an attitude or value to something that is not realistic or gets in your way of more positive relationships with yourself, others or the environment. Prejudice, for example, is a generalization which is negative and gets in your way of relating with others. Third, transferring of the learning from one situation to another is a another positive generalization. Transference affects the way that you approach learning.

1 Elegant in this instance means using the fewest processes to get the most accomplished.

Many of the problems that you may encounter in life are based upon generalizations. What you will do is reason that since this happened in the past it led to a certain outcome. Then whenever any similar situation is encountered in the present or future it will be assumed that the same outcome will be the result. This reasoning is obviously learned. Finally, generalizations delete and distort the information that is coming into and going out of your brain. Do not get the idea that this is all negative. Deletion of information is important because of how the brain works. In order to place anything into long-term memory the brain encodes and classifies whatever is important to remember. This encoding involves deleting the information so that it can be placed into the brain in a simple form. The encoded information can be retrieved with a minimum of problems. As far as distortion is concerned, the information is obviously distorted because during the encoding process so much of it has been separated from the original experience that it can easily be associated with a multitude of other experiences. Probably the most troubling and most enjoyable aspect of being human is our emotional response ability. Emotions can be a source of great pleasure or a source of deep torment. All primates, including humans have five basic emotions. These basic emotions are *fear, anger, sadness, joy,* and *disgust.* The other emotions (e.g. frustration, surprise, or excitement) are blends or variations of these five. Human emotional reactions are generalizations. They are based more on associations and assumptions than on reality. Whenever you are experiencing an emotion the brain is automatically shifting through a myriad of previous episodes and outcomes and judging which are the most appropriate for the course of action in the present situation. The implication here is that many of your emotional reactions are, again, learned. You will recall that the beginning of emotional responding is in utero. The when, how much, to whom, for what reason, and where appropriate is learned. This learning can partially be in utero, after birth, and possibly even through genetic inheritance.

Barring some sort of accident, disease, or brain surgery, it is virtually impossible to change your emotions. With this being so, the only thing left to do is to get at the way that you are responding emotionally. This means going deeply into the hidden processing of your unconscious and communicating with it. Talking therapies make assumptions through the client's overt behavior, both verbally and non-verbally, regarding unconscious processes. Whatever point of view the therapist follows, that is how (s)he will respond to the verbal and non-verbal cues. That is, if the client says certain things or acts a particular way the therapist tends to label what is being done or said and will treat the individual according to the label. Even if the therapist is rather "eclectic" there is still the tendency to label. This labeling process comes mainly from the training that the therapist had undergone. The labeling limits how the therapist will respond and treat the client. There is a way of bypassing the conscious processes and communicating directly with the unconscious. This method is what is being called *Psychokinesiology* (Pk). It is probably the clearest means of communicating with the unconscious and it may very well be the future of therapy. It is fast and elegant, efficient, and most of all, effective. The basic process itself has been in existence since the 1960s and has been applied with a good deal of success to health care. Originally it was called Applied Kinesiology (AK) and it was the development of Dr. George Goodheart, a chiropractor. What Dr. Goodheart had discovered was that there is a relationship between the way that the external muscles of the body react and what is going on inside. Originally he noticed that major muscle groups were related to certain organs in the body. As the energy of the organ became depleted the corresponding muscle group weakened. By treating the muscle groups in specific ways the corresponding organ improved and so did the patient's health. What Dr. Goodheart had found was a reliable method of getting feedback about what is going on inside of the body through the way that the body itself reacts naturally.

About the same time that Dr. Goodheart was developing Applied Kinesiology a psychiatrist named Dr. John Diamond had become frustrated because he found many of his patients came to depend on him for their healing. He also noticed that the longer that the patient stayed in therapy the more devitalized and depressed the patient became. This began to affect him. Even though he was giving his patients more understanding and the benefit of his knowledge he was somehow lowering both his own and his patient's energy levels. So, his approach was to treat his patients not as a set of psychiatric problems but in relation to the physical conditions which came to be associated with the psychiatric problems.

What he began to do is to practice what he termed "preventive medicine." He sought to raise the patient's energy level in order to overcome the physiological and psychological problems that may occur in the future. With this in mind Dr. Diamond began to use nutrition and natural supplements instead of drugs as well as physical and postural therapies. In this way Dr. Diamond began to treat the whole person. His main limitation was that he had to find out what each particular body needed and he had no way of knowing that.

About fifteen years after Dr. Goodheart developed Applied Kinesiology Dr. Diamond found out about this development. He became immediately attracted to the idea and began to study all that he could about AK. With AK, Dr. Diamond felt that he had a way of integrating his preventive medicine with each individual patient. Instead of the therapist being the one responsible for the patient's change, the patient became solely responsible. Further, the medicine that the patient used was more natural and naturally increased the health of the mind and the body.

The first thing that many therapists will say is that there is no evidence that the main technique of Applied Kinesiology, muscle testing, actually works. This is not true. Since 1981 there has been research on muscle testing and since the early 1990s more research has been conducted outside of the chiropractic journals. In one study it was found that there is a neurological basis for manual muscle testing. In another study psychological kinesiology dream interpretation was found to be a powerful intervention technique. There are also other examples of studies which have in one way or another shown the efficacy of muscle testing as a means of communicating with the unconscious.

Muscle testing is reliable and accurate. In the hands of a well-trained practitioner quite a bit of valuable information can be brought to the surface in such a way that the client goes through little, if any, emotional cathartic episodes.

Without the catharsis the client is able to see his/her problems shown from a perspective that is truly a learning experience. Then, through some specific techniques the unconscious resources are realigned and brought into harmony with the change being desired.

The most basic principle of *Psychokinesiology* is that the mind and body work in harmony. Since this is a known fact then by testing the body the internalizations of the mind can be exposed. The mind/body connection has been known for centuries but the extent of that harmony has not been deeply understood until recently. It is a well-known fact that there is a positive feedback loop between the mind and body. Even when the experience is negative, this feedback loop is still positive. One way to explain this feedback loop is through the concept of the self-fulfilling prophecy. In essence, the self-fulfilling prophecy says that if you have a conviction concerning some aspect of your environment or yourself, you will unconsciously be motivated to experience the results of that conviction. Let us say that you had been told that you are a failure and you had came to be convinced of it. You would do everything possible, on the unconscious level, to get in your way and sabotage whatever you do. Then maybe you had that previous conviction changed or had it reframed. What you thought was failure is now feedback from which to learn. You will begin to see changes in the ways that you are acting toward life and how you will be approaching life.

The fact of the matter is that people are reacting through their filters of the world and not directly on their world experience. These filters come from both genetics and environment. The vast majority of these filters were learned. It is the interpretations (one set of filters) of the environment that causes most of the emotional overreactions.

Alfred Korzybski, the founder of General Semantics, coined the phrase, "The map is not the territory." Essentially this means that human beings create models of the world in order to make sense of their experience. These maps are important filters through which we view the environment and which guide our behavior. These maps are learned and are generalizations. Consequently information is deleted and distorted in order to fit into "the territory." This "territory" is seen through the behaviors which accompany the self-fulfilling prophecy. *Psycho-kinesiology* can find the precise filters thus allowing for the reconstructing of the "map."

A second principle of *Psychokinesiology* is that many of our emotional responses were learned or given to us. Some of those given to us were given in utero others were handed down genetically and still others were taught to us after birth. Those which were learned after birth came from several different processes:

1) Imitation and modeling. Simply, whatever the child sees it will imitate and if it works or (s)he gets rewarded for it then the behavior will continue; 2) Standard conditioning procedures. Emotions are a natural way of dealing with the environment for all mammals. It is part of their survival system. The way that we respond, how we respond, to whom

we are responding in a particular way, when we are responding, and how much emotional expression we are using are rewarded and whatever is rewarded will be continued. All of the ways that we respond emotionally are classically conditioned; and 3) Through some "flash of insight." This flash of insight may be nothing more than a previously unexperienced association to a situation. Through this association an emotional response is expressed and it may or may not work.

Since emotional responses are habitual and unconscious their source can be found through the use of muscle testing and once their source is exposed the responses can be changed. What a successful Pk practitioner can do is to find out which emotional responses belong to the client and which are not. With this the individual can have a better understanding of what emotional responding (s)he is responsible for.

A third principle of *Psychokinesiology* is that problematic behaviors come from dysfunctional emotional responding. This means that the emotion itself is not the problem. It is the way that the emotion is being expressed through a confused interpretation of the situation, the environment and its possible outcome that is the problem. This interpretation had been learned. Once the dysfunctional responding has been brought out it can be dealt with. Then appropriate emotional responding in specific situations will be the result.

It is a fact that literally all of your behaviors (this includes emotional reactions, attitudes, values, etc.) have a positive intent behind them. Even those behaviors which are getting in your way now at one time had a positive intent. The reason that you continue doing them is the reward or expected reward from performing them. It is when a positively intended behavior does not get the appropriate results that it becomes dysfunctional. It is not until you realize that this behavior is getting in your way that you will decide to do something about it.

A fourth principle of *Psychokinesiology* is that each person has all of the resources that (s)he needs in order to make the changes that are needed in life. It is simply a matter of taking those behaviors, attitudes, values, beliefs, and emotions that were getting in your way and finding the areas in which they can actually be resources. It is also opening yourself up so that you can use more effectively and appropriately the resources that you already have. Through Pk testing those responses which are getting in the way are found, the resources realigned, and the unconscious is set free to bring up resources which are more appropriate and useful. From the position of having been through the experience both the conscious and unconscious minds can work together to find more appropriate methods of dealing with life's situations.

Essentially, Pk builds on the existing resources. This means that every behavior is useful in some context. Consequently, there is no attempt to change anything because all of the resources are already in operation and operating perfectly for what they are doing. All that is necessary is to allow the brain and personal experience to work together to reorganize the resources so that the mind and body are operating cooperatively and synergistically.

The fifth principle of *Psychokinesiology* is that each person can change in ways that will positively affect their life. It is important to realize that there are no mistakes, no failures, only feedback. Through feedback each person can see what needs to be done differently. Once the problematic responses have been adjusted then it becomes much easier to see what is necessary to do and plans can be made to change in such a way that positive results occur. What *Psychokinesiology* does is affect the brain in a way that it automatically begins to make different associations producing a wider variety of possibilities thus creating more opportunity for change.

The sixth principle of *Psychokinesiology* is that change can occur quickly and easily. It has been stated that the brain can learn instantly and can remember for a life-time. Through the process of *Psychokinesiology* useful change can be experienced extremely quickly. This change is on the unconscious level at first and will express itself on the conscious level in a way that will be most appropriate to the individual for that time. The fact is that most people who have undergone a Pk *Resource Realigning* have had an almost immediate subjective experience of something being changed. Others have noticed as they had gone on in their daily experiences that they are acting differently in many situations. Still others had friends or family tell them that there is something different about them. Of those who have noticed little or no change externally, there were other things which they noticed had changed (e.g. their dreams are different).

The seventh principle of *Psychokinesiology* is that life can be fun and we can learn from the fun times as well as those trying or emotionally upsetting experiences. Most people think that life has to be a struggle and that in order to learn anything you have to go through ordeals which will try the patience of Job. Not many people think that it is possible to learn from the good and fun times. What Pk does is brings the fun back into life's learning experiences. It takes the fear out of change and makes it comfortable and easy.

Psychokinesiology is about personal change. For the therapist it is a means of finding out quickly and elegantly what is getting in the way of the client's ability to change. Then it is clearing the way for unconscious change. For the client it is a way of confronting those bothersome problems which have been interfering with the enjoyment of life in a simple, easy, effective, and unobtrusive manner.

Psychokinesiology uses the basic techniques of Applied Kinesiology and adds to it other key ingredients which direct it toward psychological intervention. You will find that there is a relationship between the organs of the body and specific emotional reactions. Chinese medicine had noticed this millennia ago. It was not until the first part of the 20th century that psychologists "discovered" a connection between the organs and some psychological problems. This was noticed in the process known as organ language. At present, psychoneuroimmunologists have found that repressed emotions are held and stored in the body. Once these emotional memories are released then both physiological and psychological problems can be cleared away. In Pk by testing specific organs while considering the problem and examining related emotions the underlying sources to the problem can be exposed and dealt with. Once this is done then the resources can be realigned. After this realigning is done then better choices are possible.

Psychokinesiology is a mind and life expanding experience. It is fascinating to hear from clients who are really taking responsibility for their lives. They invariably see themselves and their lives from a different perspective thus being able to gain a different insight into the choices that they have been making. With a different understanding their lives tend to readjust their worldview bringing with it another kind of emotional reaction more appropriate to the experience. It is this flash of understanding that we have when we discover something new and different about ourself and our life. When we have had that experience we can then fathom more about the depths of our inner selves.

A word of caution: The techniques in this book are extremely effective and *will* cause change when used properly. The appropriate training with their proper use is the best way to understand their full potential.

Even one who has had previous training with AK may find using some of these techniques somewhat confusing at first, consequently, training in the techniques will circumvent many initial problems with their use. Also, what you will be reading about here is a basic program. There are other techniques that increase the effectiveness of the system.

CHAPTER 1

UNDERSTANDING CONSCIOUSNESS

Our reality is perceived through whatever state of consciousness we are in at the time. So, our consciousness is based on our sensory experience. In order to be conscious of anything we must be aware of what is happening inside and outside of our body. The awareness of what is happening inside and outside of our body makes up our reality. Our reality, then, takes in not just physical objects but emotions such as love, hate and fear, our relationships, our attitudes, and all of our emotion-based responses as well as everything related to those responses.

A major fact about how the brain works is that most of what it does is aimed toward survival. Consciousness is only a small portion of what the brain does. If you look at how the brain is put together you can see this to be true. Initially a sensation moves through the brain stem, through the cerebellum, cerebrum, and the pons. These are the older portions of the brain. Here we find all of the basic survival systems. Then it goes into the limbic system with its emotional survival controls. Finally it reaches the neo-cortex and the more advanced portions such as the decision-making aspects of the frontal lobes. In all, at least ninety percent of the brain works to keep us alive. The creative awareness of consciousness is only a small portion of brain functioning.

Consciousness can be defined as simply as *a state of awareness*. It is a process of being aware or *knowing*. As awareness it is modified by the construction of and by the processes that we call "the mind." Consequently, consciousness is more than a simple state of awareness. Essentially, in order to experience anything, we must have the consciousness for it. That is, we must be aware of the *possibility* of its existence. This state of awareness is the basic knowledge or thought of the possibility that something exists or can happen. Without the basic knowledge of a thing's possibility it will not be experienced. Consciousness, though, is extremely difficult to define because it is *a set of processes in the brain.* The mind is also a set of processes in the brain. Both are interconnected.

Defining consciousness as simply a state of awareness does not take into account all of what consciousness involves. It is a subjective experience that involves the processes of perception, learning, thinking, memory and emotion. Therefore, our ability to react to our environment is influenced by our state of consciousness.

Consciousness has been seen as a constantly changing continuum or stream of thought. This is due to it shifting regularly from object to object, from inside to outside and back again. It is an emergent property of the brain. This means that consciousness arises from the brain. Since it does arise from the brain it is easy to assume that the neurons may very well be the basis of consciousness. This is not so. Neurons may be associated with consciousness but they are not the basis of it. They are most likely associated with brain events at a certain level of consciousness in certain regions of the brain. This is only speculation.

The most necessary condition for consciousness is attention but *attention* is not identified with any particular mental function. Attention is mainly the process of *selection* of what to focus on at any particular time. Consciousness is not identified with focused attention. You must, though, have focused attention in order to experience an event.

There are both active and passive aspects of consciousness just as there are active and passive aspects in attention. Sensation and perception are both passive aspects of consciousness. Deliberate choice (free will) is active. It is the use of both these active and passive aspects which create consciousness from its different properties.

Researchers are looking into the individual aspects of consciousness: the how, the what and so on. It may very well be that consciousness requires a feedback loop between the perceiver and the perceived as well as an innate understanding of possibilities. This concept has been postulated by theoretical physicists. What the physicists are saying is that the perceiver and the perceived are interconnected. Whatever you are perceiving is somehow perceiving you. It is this reciprocal perception which creates consciousness. Hence, we are intimately tied to the universe and it to us. All our intentions, our emotions, our desires, our dreams, our actions, as well as our thoughts have an effect on the universe. It is through consciousness that we become an individual separate from all else.Consciousness is at the basis of everything and it exists without being associated with any living system. It is the creative element of the universe. Without it nothing would be able to appear. So, no matter what our conceived realities appear to be, we must be conscious of them in order to be able to perceive them. Consciousness is not thoughts and thinking. Thoughts and thinking are only the *after-effects,* the epiphenomena if you will, of consciousness. Consciousness is at the basis of perception. This implies that there are different states of awareness. In actuality, for everything that is experienced there are as many different states of consciousness as there are for each and every reality which can be perceived. It has been postulated that realities sort of create each other by being self-excited systems and that they are brought into being by the participation of those who participate. Remember we are all active participants in the universe through our choices and not passive observers. We all create our experience of reality.

Consciousness began probably before infancy. While in the womb the fetus becomes aware of different states that are experienced by the mother. Whenever the mother feels any emotion, so also does the fetus. Whenever the mother speaks or hears any loud enough sounds, the fetus hears it. So, the basic states of awareness, the initial experiences of consciousness began in utero. After birth the infant begins to associate those experiences to his own personal experiences and expands his awareness and his consciousness.

Consciousness is organized into a hierarchy of mental or psychic elements This does not mean that there is such a thing as "higher" or "lower" states of consciousness. The words higher and lower are terms which do not really have any importance or meaning. What constitutes that generally considered "higher" consciousness is the value or the value change that becomes attached to the state itself. Often one assumes that a state reached is "higher" if it activates the emotions sufficiently to motivate a differing set of values. These values are usually more altruistic and selfless. If the values and their accompanying behaviors are temporary or need to be reinforced constantly then the state was not one of "higher" consciousness.

Consciousness could be nothing more than a specific repetitive process in the brain. It may be the individual's experience of the brain's reverberating process of the automatic command to search for more information. Attached to this is the recharging of its nerve cell assemblies and its perceptions. If so, this would enable the brain to plan and prepare for each subsequent action on the basis of past action, sensory input, and perceptual blending. Simply put, an act of perception is not the copying of an incoming stimulus. It is a step in a path by which the brain grows, reorganizes itself and reaches into its internal environment to change it to its own advantage. Consciousness is stabilized by simply keeping the brain busy. As long as there is input coming into or being created by the brain consciousness will be the result.

Consciousness is closely aligned to our perception of reality. The reality we perceive reacts in a particular way to our awareness of it. We in turn react to that awareness in a particular way. As soon as an action is performed and observed, it alters both the actor's and the observer's reality instantly. Observation disturbs the unbroken wholeness of the universe. It is through the act of observation that each observer separates himself from the rest of creation. Observation brings in knowledge. The price of this knowledge is that of becoming increasingly more alone and isolated. This isolation is the feeling of estrangement from the wholeness of the universe.

To be conscious of something means that at a certain point in time we have conceived of its existence. Consciousness is both awareness and the creation of experience; the being and knowing of experience. Consciousness seems to stream into us from outside in the form of sense perceptions. Sense perceptions tell us *that* something is but not *what* something is. What something is comes to us through the process of *apperception*. Apperception may be either directed, as attention, or undirected as fantasy or daydreaming. For the main function of consciousness is to recognize and assimilate the external world through the senses. It then translates into visible reality the world within us. We will then experience what is actually within us. Consequently, the only things we experience immediately are the contents of consciousness. What this means is that we have brought something into our sphere of reality and we have experienced it; or rather as much of it as our limitations would allow. Understand that consciousness actually conceives while thinking adapts that conception.

The world we perceive consists not of things but of interactions. What we experience is not external reality, but our interaction with it. It is only through contact with things that our self-consciousness comes into contact with the world and vice-versa. We can never really know what an object is, only what it does.

The attributes that objects contain belong to interactions, not to autonomously existing things. All things in the universe which appear to exist autonomously are actually parts of one all-encompassing natural pattern. No parts of that pattern are ever really separated from it or each other. In theoretical physics, Bell's Theorem states that particles once in contact will continue to influence one another no matter how far apart they are. Consequently, there is no such thing as separate parts. Everything is interconnected.

Thoughts are the programs to our brain. But our thoughts are affected by our reality (and vice-versa) as well as by our consciousness. Consciousness underlies all experience. Without a certain level of awareness we could not perceive of the reality at that level.

Our thoughts tell us exactly what our reality is. They tell us what to expect and what not to expect. They tell us who we are. They give us an indication of what we think our place in the vast scheme of things is. These are the programs which are put into our brains. Our brains will do the processing. The output is our perceived actuality.

Our willful thoughts may not even reflect what is deep within our mind. They are more or less a mediator with our external environment. These willful thoughts contain a lot of repressed materials concerning mainly what we feel about ourself, our environment and what we think we deserve from life. Everything that we perceive is an offspring of our willed intentions. All of our activities as well as our thoughts have intent behind them. We have the ability to choose what we will intend to happen. It is this conscious ability to choose that sets humankind above the lower forms of life on this planet. We can choose how and what we will experience as well as how we will react or act to it.

A question then arises about all that we are experiencing in our world today. What we are perceiving as reality is a combination of our own consciousness as well as all consciousnesses existing today. Consequently, everyone who is alive today is actively involved in creating our experience of reality as we know it. Perceived reality is, then, the creation of all conscious choosing entities combined.

Everything we perceive is not a solid and stable object. It is in constant flux. Those things which do not appear to be changing are changing at a much slower rate than those things which are changing quickly. If we could actually perceive what everything actually is it would appear to be a myriad of dancing atoms moving at an amazing speed. Our senses can only perceive things which are moving much slower. So everything appears to be stable and unmoving.

Every experience we have encountered and learned has affected what we perceive and vice-versa. These are all part of the structure of our consciousness. We are most assuredly not aware of the fact that these experiences are doing anything to us but this is occurring just the same. As we have seen, something must be part of our consciousness before we will be able to experience it. So, being part of our consciousness it has an effect on us as we encounter and experience it.

The current view of consciousness is that it appears to come from some sort of particle reaction taking place at the synapse, the space between the nerve cells. Consciousness, as well as every other experience, is nothing more than a series of chemical reactions in the brain. Looking at sensory input our sense organs are the perceptors. Within the perceptors are the neurons and the neural connections going into the brain. Once the perceptual neurons have been stimulated their reactions are all *exactly* the same going into the brain. It is where these neural reactions are going which determine what is being experienced.

It has been theorized that every neuron is like part of a hologram. That is, it contains the consciousness of the total organism. This implies that every neuron is involved in every experience. It really does not matter whether the experience is an external physical activity or internalized as a thought. Even a passing thought would most probably be a simple reflection of some inner need or desire associated with our consciousness. A constant thought would most assuredly be the programmer of the brain. Even to experience a thought we must first be conscious of the possibility of the thought itself. The consciousness for that thought must then be contained in a particular set of neurons.

All information we receive needs to be processed. This processing leaves a neural trace or neural image in the neurons. Whenever our brain makes associations it searches through these neural images in the form of chemicals in the synapses. If there is a problem with our view of reality it is seen in the associations our brain makes. A psychotic individual has problems with reality testing. In reality testing a person appraises and evaluates the inner and external possibilities for the successful satisfaction of all aspects of an experience. The psychotic makes convoluted associations due to a misconstrued consciousness. The resulting behavior becomes a problem to both the individual and to those around that individual.

We are constantly constructing our reality through our choices. These choices are very highly influenced by our conditioning and the experiences which surround that conditioning. From this experience we respond according to the results we *assume* we are going to have.

What we perceive is constantly being modified. On the conscious level, though, it appears to remain the same. Our senses perceive everything statically and without change or motion (discontinuously). This is an innate tendency because a constantly changing universe would be almost impossible to comprehend. We need a certain degree of stimulus change in order to stimulate the senses. Stimulus change makes our experience interesting.

We make the mistake of assuming that our universe never changes because our perceptions appear, on the surface, as unchanging. This is the illusion created by the fallibility of our senses and the point of space-time at which we, as an energy form, exist. As a result, our view of our reality and our level of reality remain pretty much static. From time to time we will experience alterations of our consciousness. We run headlong into these alterations mostly when we are forced into it. One of the major changes experienced is when we find out that we have aged and that we cannot do the same things we could in our younger days. We must adjust our consciousness at this point to fit into our lifestyle. Then there are people who will desperately attempt to hold on to the consciousness that is totally out of synchronicity with their existence instead of allowing themselves to grow, to learn and to pass on their experience with dignity.

Our perceptions are consciousness-based and reality-directed. Whatever we perceive on the physical level is based on our state of consciousness and directed by what we view reality to be. Perception, consciousness and reality are an interconnected and intertwined trinity. We cannot have a perception which does not exist in a reality for which we have not the consciousness. If it does not exist in our consciousness, it does not exist for us. That does not mean that at some time later it still will not exist or in some previous time it had existed. Once we become aware, on a deeper level, of an existence, and it of us, it then is on the way to becoming part of our physical actuality. Also, we can set a reality into motion by making ourself aware of that thing. This creates the consciousness for that reality. This awareness brings about the possibility for that concept to become a perception in actuality.

Our perceptions are constantly being modified although consciously they appear to be the same. Our senses perceive everything statically and without change or motion. This process affects our consciousness so that we are aware of only those things which do not appear to be dynamic.

Our perceptions are founded upon our state of consciousness and governed by our physical actuality. Whatever we perceive on the objective level is based upon our state of consciousness and the processes involved in that consciousness and directed by what we assume reality to be. We cannot have a perception that does not exist in our conception of reality. If it does not exist in our conception of reality then we do not have the consciousness for it at all. If it does not exist in our consciousness then it does not exist for us *alone*.

Consciousness affects us on all levels of our existence. Prenatal awareness exists and it has an effect on our life even though we have no realization of it. We know that the fetus is aware of sound vibrations and things said prior to birth. With this knowledge it is more than a possibility at some level of awareness that this is transferred into an individual's lifestyle. There is evidence for this found by some non-traditional therapists and hypnotherapists doing age regressions. More recently it was found out that during the last few months of pregnancy the fetus can hear. Postnatal researchers found specific infant reactions thus proving the observation. Consequently, not only does life outside of the womb affect us and our consciousness, it seems that prior to birth there is also a level of awareness that has an effect as well.

We have a rather unique ability for becoming conscious of many different realities and experiencing them in different ways. We can react to many different consciousnesses and become intimately aware of them. Every consciousness has its own special uniqueness which gives it an individual perception of those things existing outside of it. We, on the other hand, have the ability to experience many different states of consciousness . . . and return to give others that experience through the use of language. In essence, our consciousness can transcend time, space and dimension. With alterations of consciousness we can gain greater insight into our own created universe as well as the universe at large.

Our consciousness is not without limitations. First, it is limited by reason of being human consciousness. That is, it is associated with a finite being. Second, our consciousness is limited by the experience of the senses bringing the information into our brain. Third, it has limitations placed on it for no other reason than that of coming into existence in association with biochemical constructs. Hence, it has basic limitations provided by genetics and nature. Fourth, our consciousness is limited by the conditioning procedures that it encounters from the very onset of birth. This includes all of the learning experiences available to the individual. Finally, consciousness is limited by the society and all of its processes, philosophies and institutions. The more limitations, the more constricted the consciousness. This means nothing more than the simple fact that we become less and less aware of our experience and more and more aware of the external restrictions.

Consciousness alters the world by altering us. It affects our evaluation of the future by altering our perceptions. Our perceptions in turn affect our consciousness. Consequently, as you can see, consciousness, perceptions, behavior, and experience (mental and physical) are constantly interacting. All of these are continually influencing our choices. It is our choices which create the universe, or the part of it that we will be experiencing.

Now that you have a more in depth understanding of what consciousness is as well as what it does, understanding altered states of consciousness is necessary. An altered state of consciousness is anything that can alter our perception of our reality in some way. In essence, an altered state of consciousness is a basic shift in awareness. Once this has occurred, the world will be viewed as primarily and organizationally different than we are used to seeing it. This can reach all the way down into the deeper levels of the self and perception. From here we will be viewing everything from another perspective. Our whole experience can take on a new meaning once this happens.

We experience slight alterations of consciousness constantly. As soon as we notice something different about an object, it is due to a shift in our awareness at the time. Whenever we experience new knowledge of ourself or part of our existence which causes a change in behavior, attitude, viewpoint, and so forth, we have undergone another shift.

Whenever we go to sleep and dream we are in a totally different consciousness. The use of drugs, alcohol, hypnosis, meditation, and so on all bring us into different altered states of consciousness.

One of the human being's greatest assets is the ability to adjust to change. In order to make this adjustment there must be an alteration of consciousness, a difference in awareness, in the view of reality, and in thinking. If one of these four concepts is unable to be changed then the adjustment is difficult or highly improbable until that level of consciousness has occurred. Adjustment begins in the brain/mind, which contains our whole universe as concepts. It is through our intentionality that we experience these concepts.

What we perceive as reality is nothing more than the created thoughts that exist in the brain. Reality can be seen as the thoughts associated with what we have previously experienced as being real. We have seen that there is no reality until that reality is perceived. So, reality depends directly upon the choices of what and how we choose to observe. Those choices depend on the content of our thoughts. Our thoughts depend on our expectation and our desires for consistency in our experience.

It does not matter how accurate our interpretation of reality may be. Our perception of reality is directly related to what we were taught reality is *supposed* to be. So, our reality can be defined in terms of *experience* both past and present.

Whenever we observe an object as a solid, we are forced to choose what to observe. If it is seen as an abstract form, there is no choice. The construction of what we see is through the choice of the available alternatives. This construction process continues throughout our lives.

The term reality is derived from the word *res*, which means *thing*, and *revi*, which means *think*. Reality is then everything about which we can think. Probably the best way to define reality is: all of the stimuli available to us at a certain moment in time and point in space. This definition opens up the experience of reality-upon-reality. We can gain insight into an individual by how (s)he appears to be interpreting their reality.

With a level of consciousness and reality at a certain point, we will constantly experience everything associated with those levels. What we will be doing with our choices is altering the *potential* reality to make it actual. The choices we make are essentially based on the image of the behaviors we see ourself performing and the outcomes we have associated with the performance of the actions. All of this has a basis in past experience. It is established upon the information that had been received, not on the information that is currently being experienced. The information we received in the past is never really lost. What we do by having this past information is to alter the potential reality making it actual.

All we perceive outside of ourself has been given the general term of "reality." Everything we perceive is nothing more than *external representations* of *internal concepts.* We can essentially say that what we perceive as reality is nothing more than the mental fabrications present in our brain. Essentially, our reality is the thoughts which are associated with what we have previously experienced as being "real." In fact, reality does not exist until that reality is perceived. The reality we perceive depends directly upon our choices of what and how we choose to observe. Those choices depend on the substance of our thoughts. Our thoughts depend on our expectations and our need for consistency.

When it is said that reality is, "All the stimuli available . . ." it means not only what is seen on the surface but also our interpretation of that stimuli. According to modern scientific knowledge, we receive about ten thousand bits of stimulation per second in our eyes alone. Since this information comes to us in bits, this means that the basic structure of nature is non-integrated, granular, or discontinuous. Consequently, trying to take in all of this information at once can easily overload our neural circuitry. Hence, we selectively choose to what we will respond.

Now, choosing what we will respond to is a rather complicated process. For we have parts of our brain, the reticular activating system for example, which unconsciously preselects stimuli for our experience. Other stimuli can have highly emotional experiences attached to it and we will repress it either consciously or unconsciously. There may also be stimuli which will cause total system overload and it will shut-down (i.e. faint).

Not only do we have to consider the present experience and our natural automatic censoring devices but we must also consider the stimulation brought about through previous learning experiences. Through this we will learn how to respond, when to respond, and to what we will respond. It also defines our reality and our experience of reality. This cannot be changed by anything that we do in the present.

Essentially, we can say that all of the realities that we perceive directly are related to our unconscious thought processes and beliefs. All reality, then, is learned. To the extent that we believe that reality to be true, it will come to be true. If it does not exist on physical reality for you, it does not matter how strongly you profess a belief in it, you actually do not believe in it. Even if it does come into "existence" for you (via hallucinations, delusions, etc.) that does not mean it exists for anyone else.

It is important to remember that the existence or nonexistence of any reality is simply a matter of choice. We choose whatever we have decided to make "real" in our life. We choose whatever we have decided to experience in our life. We choose whatever we have decided our life to be. No one or nothing outside of ourself "makes" us choose, controls us or in any way manipulates us so that we will do, say, or think a certain thing. This happens only when we allow this to happen by giving ourself and our lives over to that person or group. We are free to choose. We construct our reality every instant of our conscious lives through our choices. Reality, will, become whatever we choose it to be.

The fact is the world exists only as possibility until it is observed. Further, what we perceive as a reality is a perception of only a small portion of what we understand reality to be. All things exist potentially as different combinations of other things. Each combination has a certain probability of occurring. Each part of the objective actuality is produced by all other parts and its appearance is based on the interdependence of all things existing.

What appears to be "real" objects are actually passing illusions which result from our limited sensory systems. The illusion is that the parts of a complete essence are actual objects or *observables*. Self-actualization is the experience that objects, including "I," are only fleeting substances stripped of their separate realities; momentary links between illusions of the past and the future expanding in the illusion of time.

Three kinds of reality have been speculated:
1. *The Measurable Reality* which is the physical, knowable reality of the senses.
2. Thoughts, dreams, and pictures that symbolize or resemble the external reality. This is *The Reality of the Mind*; the world of archetypes as described by Jung.
3. The *Intermediary Reality* containing the attributes of both realities

at the same time. All realities are seen as superpositioned or, rather, superimposed upon each other.

In the third reality cause and effect are evident. It is not physical objects which follow these laws, but phantoms of a different form of matter. The only thing they depend on for their operation is space and time, for they change in very orderly, causal ways when they are not observed and disturbed. There is no possible way to observe without actively interfering with and disturbing what is being observed. Hence, there is no such thing as an unbiased observer. As soon we observe anything, we immediately disturb it from the particle level thus affecting it. The simple act of observation changes an object forever. It is this act of willful observation which creates the world we see.

There are those who will claim it does not matter that particles are disturbed. With something as complex as a human being this idea seems meaningless. The fact remains that, as soon as the particles of an object are disturbed, the whole object is changed. In cybernetics it is stated that if one part of the system is changed, it changes the whole system. Literally the results of all research is dependable *temporarily*. That means it is basically biased by the willful observations and choices of the researchers. Recall the old adage: "The truths of one era are the myths of the next."

For reality to exist, there must be the thought, the intent, for its existence by an infinite number of universes. Simply, all beings who are part of a certain universe and who themselves are other smaller universes create the different realities of the grand universe. Their intent to create or bring something into some objective reality creates this.

At the very basis of existence in a reality is the initial plan, thought, and creation of that reality. Without this initial *intent* neither the thought of nor production of that reality could possibly exist. It is possible that a reality may come into existence through the intent of a single intender. This is difficult because many reality levels have to be changed in order to do this. In other words, at some point there has to be cooperation from other reality levels or intenders in order for existence to occur.

As soon as the initial design for a reality is made, it is necessary that consciousness be altered in order to adjust to the new reality. As soon as the new reality begins to become created, other separate but equally real inner and outer realities are created to aid the individual in organizing all that is necessary perceive that reality. So, what we have is the creation of a limited organizational system which will perceive a confined, created experience of the universe.

The basic structure of the physical world is determined by how we choose to look at it. How we understand our reality to be is a creation of our mind.

Whatever we truly believe to be real will be real. Whatever we, through our basic intent bring into our outer awareness, will be. As members of the universe, we are constantly in a process of becoming. Our realities are constantly changing as are our perceptions of those realities. Consequently, nothing remains the same for more than a fraction of a second. As soon as it is perceived, it is changed. In order to make the world more stable, we perceive the physical world and the objects in it as simply being there; being what they are without change, and at times, moving from point to point. Nevertheless, everything is part of a harmonious, flowing unity. Just as the hallucination and delusion are "real" to the psychotic, so also are the myriad of objects that we perceive real to us. We created them with the assistance of all the other intents of all other existences.

Our experience of reality is a personal one. How we relate to our reality is also personal. As long as we accept the realities we have constructed as being "The Truth" we cannot fully experience nor relate to ourselves or our reality. We also cannot relate to our reality when we have forced some unrealistic change of our perception upon our reality. We are, then, cutting ourselves off from part of the potential experience of reality which is possible.

Researchers talk about the mind as mechanistic and finite and operating in real time. That is, it is a mechanism for manipulating symbols for the processing of information. Perception, understanding, and learning are not just a matter of following distinct rules for a particular result, but holistic processes. They make possible our interaction with the world. This means that the mind is made up of a large number of little processors or agents each of which makes connections between things and keeps lists of what things are useful in what circumstances. Thus, all knowledge in the mind is manifest in the connections the brain makes.

The mind/body problem mainly concerns itself with the problem of understanding the relationship between the physical and the metaphysical. This relationship occurs through the fleeting, though personally real, world of the mind and the complex dynamics of the physical body. Even though there are areas of changeability in the link between the mind and the body, we tend to assume that a set of rules limits this changeability.

The idea that the mind and body are separate things is no longer considered. Recent developments in neurochemistry have changed that. Our whole existence including consciousness has been found to be a matter of brain chemistry.

The idea that brain impulses are transmitted chemically, not electrically, revolutionized our thinking about the brain. This had a direct effect on our concepts of mental illness and thinking itself. Researchers have confirmed that thinking positive thoughts affects the neurotransmitters. Positive thinking and actions bring about more positive hormonal and neurotransmitter changes. The use of meditation, visual imagery, directed concentration, and so on actually affects the neural pathways. Research has verified that hormones change during meditation and directed concentration. Hormones, it is known, eventually affect the whole system.

All human experience is being broken down to simply a matter of brain chemistry. Any adjustments to that chemistry is seen to come through conditioning and learning. As a human animal, we all have particular chemical reactions which are innate (i.e. emotional reactions are essentially reflexive) but our interpretations of those chemical reactions in our body is learned. All learning is simply a matter of chemical reactions. Learning is essentially the conditioning or entrainment of chemical reactions. Religious experience, for example, is a matter of chemistry with the ramification that any deity which exists does so only within the consciousness of the individual thinking particular thoughts of that deity. Peak experiences, the experience of self-actualization, individuation, and so forth are all likewise a matter of chemistry. We actively create our personal universe from our personal experience. Our experience is a matter of chemistry and chemical compositions and reactions. All our thoughts, beliefs, attitudes, talents, abilities, etc. are chemical reactions. Any permanent change in the chemistry can change our whole existence.

The only true constant in the universe is change. Absolutely nothing is as it appears to be. It is in constant flux and is in the process of changing. We cannot wear the same clothes we wore when we were two years old. Many want to hold on to concepts, ideas, beliefs, and their associated behaviors which are at an immature stage of development and which do not really work. When doing this we actually restrict our potential, our ability to advance, and to create a different experience of our universe. We are all born with particular abilities, and with others that can be developed. Some of these exceptional abilities include a photographic or eidetic memory and the ability to do super-fast calculations, the ability to do remote viewing and absent healing, creative genius and creative altruism, the ability to do spontaneous remissions, and voluntary control of the mind/body functions. These abilities, which we all possess to some degree, challenge the sufficiency of our existing scientific models of human performance and individual beliefs about the limits of personal perfection and achievement. These abilities are poorly understood. They are, though, conceivably of the greatest relevance. Science will eventually shed new light on the mechanisms underlying these abilities. It will yield the knowledge about the processes for optimal learning and development, as well as provide a test of the current models of mind/brain operations. Psychology can help satisfy the urge to surpass or achieve, and can help personal growth through self-knowledge and awareness. Philosophy and sociology along with scientific advances in the understanding of the mind/brain function and the psychology of human growth and development, can realize a new view of human nature and abilities. A realistic encouragement and development of these abilities will lead to more effective practices in all areas of everyday life. This will help to increase the development of human capabilities. With this view grounded in science and responsive to the individual measurements of human experience, there will be far-reaching effects for the society as a whole (i.e. the social institutions and the goals of the society).

The experience of nonordinary realities through altered states of consciousness can remind us that the world we experience is a construction of our mind. This can be done by our reestablishing of a connection with the Earth. The challenge is to encourage creative responses to the practical challenges we confront in every field of endeavor and every aspect of our lives.

A worldview is always supported by a world. The worldview structures the world we perceive. This is why we can change the world by changing our beliefs about it. Many will claim that this is not so; that you will still see the same exact world you have always seen. The fact of the matter is that if you change your beliefs about your world, yourself, and your life you will see a different perspective of life. As the conditions around you begin to change you will be forced to conclude that the world is different. You may still see the same trees, the same cars, the same people but you will see them differently. Remember, it is our beliefs about ourself and our world which shape the direction of our experiences; not the experiences themselves. We must also consider that what we view as reality is not only part of our consciousness but also part of all of the consciousnesses of everyone that exists today. It is an intermingling of all of the beliefs of everyone. Therefore, we are all responsible for the condition of the world.

Our worldview is influenced not only by the conditioning that we have encountered but also by the worldview of everyone else living. The frustration and anger we experience comes from the helplessness we feel when attempting to make an unrealistic worldview, our expectations, fit into what we really are experiencing. If we try to believe in something that does not work and does not satisfy or fit into our actual belief structure we will attempt to get others to follow what we claim to believe. The more devoid of meaning the philosophy the more we will attempt to identify with it and the stronger will be our desire to get others to follow suit. If another does follow us, the more we will be convinced that we were right. If they do not the more convinced we will be that we have to try harder the next time. We will then satisfy ourself with the rationalization that it is not us but them. There is something wrong with them for we know that we are right!

When we do finally get down to changing our beliefs we will see changes occur in our worldview. As we view these world changes, we see new facets of ourselves and new opportunities come into focus. We begin to think and act differently, and the energies of life organize themselves differently in us.

The human mind has many untapped talents. With practice, these untapped mental abilities can be used in problem solving, decision making, and living more creatively.

CHAPTER 2

HOW THE BRAIN LEARNS

When the average person talks about and experiences learning, he does not really know how to define it or explain what is going on. Psychologists look at learning as *any lasting change in behavior that results from practice*. One implication here is that something which is learned stays with you allowing for continued change in your behavior. The other implication is that practice is necessary in order to bring that change about. The brain is known to contain more neurons than there are stars in the Milky Way Galaxy (10^{12}). Each neuron has at least 1000 synapses with other neurons. This gives there more than 10^{15} connections. Consequently, it is impossible at this time to measure learning directly. We cannot go into someone's nervous system and stick electrodes in their neurons and find out which ones have changed. We also cannot go into the synapses and see which chemicals have been changed as the learning situation occurred. Consequently, the only way that we can detect if learning has taken place is by observing behavior. If behavior has changed in the direction of the training then we can assume that learning has taken place.

The brain can learn instantly and can remember for a lifetime. Every experience we have ever had is tucked away somewhere in our brain in a series of chemicals and neural pathways. We have the information there. All that is needed to get at the information are suitable prompts. It is important to realize that the whole nervous system is involved in one way or another in each learning experience.

Any learning experience that we have induces both temporary and permanent changes at many different levels within the nervous system. Researchers have found learning actually begins in the brain stem. From there it moves into the limbic system. In the limbic system deep in the center of the brain, in the hippocampus the consolidation of that learning occurs. After the consolidation of the learning it is sent on into other parts of the brain for action and to be stored as memory.

Learning does not occur in the neural pathways which are the quietest. It takes an active neurology to insure that learning occurs. Research has found that whenever an organism is placed in a stimulating environment it tends to explore much more. This exploration activates more neurons. Upon its death the organism placed in this enriching environment is found to have a heavier brain with more dendritic connections. This is a direct result of the learning experiences encountered in the environment.

Before reaching the higher processes all sensory data coming into the brain undergoes a filtering process. This filtering occurs as it passes from one neuron to another. As this information passes through each synapse it is influenced by whatever an individual is attending to and whatever it is conscious of at the time. Also, as it is passing through the synapse it is readjusting and reintegrating the biochemistry of each synapse. As each synapse is being readjusted associations are being automatically made. This has a tendency to readjust the neurons even more creating the possibility for more change. Thus potentiality is increased. From these influences further choices are made. It is the quality and quantity of the neuropeptide[1] receptors that determines these choices. The relative quality and quantity of the receptors is determined by previous experiences. Look at the brain as a tool that not only filters and stores sensory input, but associates it with other events and stimuli that occur simultaneously at any synapse or receptor along the way.

---

[1] A peptide is a compound that contains two or more amino acids linked by a carboxyl group of one amino acid and the amino group of another. Neuropeptides are peptides occurring within the neurology of the brain. One of their main jobs is the storing and transferring of information. They are also referred to as cytokines or chemokines.

When you think about it, your memory is really amazing. Imagine being able to recall something that happened to you many years ago. Even more amazing is your ability to be able to react to that experience as if you were experiencing it again. Then consider your ability to relate that experience to another with some great detail. Have you considered the simple processes involved in dealing with numbers? Do you recall having to learn the times tables, the procedures for addition, subtraction or division? Think of what it would be like if every time you had to balance your checkbook it was necessary to go to a book to look up how to add and subtract. Life would be a whole lot more difficult if humans had a highly limited memory capacity like many of the lower animals—but, then, there would be no way to for us to know we were limited.

Researchers see four levels of learning. They are in a hierarchy of increased intricacy. At the most basic level are the *molecular changes within the single neurons* themselves. Here are the ionic and essential chemical changes. The next level is *the level of communications among neurons at the synapses*. This includes all of the chemical changes which result at the synapses. At a still higher level are *circuits of interconnected neurons*. Remember that when we learn anything it sensitizes a neuronal circuit to react in a specific pattern in order to produce that experience again. Finally, at the highest level is *the activity within whole assemblies of neurons*. It is this higher activity which may control the complex patterns of behaviors we exhibit.

Much of our learning has been under conditions which can only be described as stressful. It is a fact that the neurons must be active for learning to take place. The phrase "active neurons" does not mean that the learner must be stressed. It is unfortunate that traditional education sets up circumstances which require learning to be stressful. There is the implication in education that if you are sitting up straight and attending to what the instructor is teaching, you are learning. As any teacher will tell you, this is not the case in many instances. Also the idea of competition is imbedded in western education. Competition is accompanied by stress. In our businesses stress is inherent. Look at the number of individuals who have stress-related ailments and are high-powered business persons. Stress is even part of our most intimate relationships. It should not be, but it is. Stress seems to be an ever-present part of human existence. It appears that being human and having stress are almost synonymous. Research has found that stress does have something to do with at least some types of learning. The fact is many psychological problems have some form of stress (originally referred to as anxiety) at their basis and this stress is seen in the emotional reactions associated with the experience.

Stress may enhance *some* types of learning by the release of certain biochemicals. It is known that we can learn most quickly when we are alert, attentive and somewhat stimulated by the experience. It is also known that extreme arousal impresses the experience on the psyche. An excellent example of extreme arousal is a traumatic experience. Trauma has the whole body and all of the senses in a state of arousal imbedding the experience in the nervous system. The fact of the matter is that there is a link between stress and the biochemical events underlying learning and memory. Emotions, stress and learning are linked. Remember learning does not occur in the pathways that are quietest. There must be activity in the neural pathways for learning to take place. This cannot be otherwise. In reality, stressful situations tend to play a rather significant role in psychological problems. Look at phobias as an example. A phobia is an out of proportion fear. Fear is a response that mammals have to a perceived threat. It is this perceived threat that causes the stress. Hence, a phobia is a response to a stressful situation where a threat is expected. The stress itself will produce more stress thus increasing the stressfulness. Consequently, the phobic is stressed out about the stress. In essence, he is afraid of the fear. Above this may may be self-directed anger caused by frustration due to his inability to make any headway with the phobic response. Even more so may be the anxiety created by not knowing what life would be like without the phobia. This is the main reason that a phobia appears larger than life to the phobic.

When you think about it, our ability to store, retrieve and disseminate information is a pretty amazing series of processes. These abilities give us our civilizations, our learning, our inventions and our sciences. All of these are based on having a memory which is accessible and functional. Without the ability to access stored information an individual or group cannot evolve. This may have been one of the main reasons that the Neanderthal succumbed to Cro-Magnon and early Homo Sapiens. The Neanderthal was stronger and had a larger brain cavity but Cro-Magnon and Homo Sapiens apparently had a larger cortex which allowed them to access and use more information. Cro-Magnon and Homo Sapiens appear to have had a greater capacity to invent and use weapons. They were probably more able to adapt to their changing environment as well. Further, the Cro-Magnon and Homo Sapiens seemed to be better able to pass the information on to their progeny who added to it and passed that on and so forth. From the recent research it appears that Neanderthal's saving grace may have been that of being an excellent imitator.

In the brains of higher organisms, there are copies or representations of activities which are stored when processed. The storage of this form of learning is termed *Cognitive* or *Representational Memory*. The brain's stored copy of a representation is termed a *Neuronal Assembly*. Neuronal Assemblies are coactivated sets of neurons that are capable of changing depending on experience. Certain patterns of cooperative activity might encourage and balance connections within the assembly. This multiple activation of neuronal assemblies is essential to the learning process.

Single neurons are activated with multiple transmitter signals. Thus we have one neuron being activated by the transmitter responses of many different neurons all responding to their separate input signals. Different transmitters are independently expressed and managed in the same neuron. Experience modifies neuronal expression and alters genetic clarification in the nervous system as well. In essence, experience sort of *reconstructs* part of the nervous system creating a neural pathway in order to bring about a different mode of relating to and interacting with the environment. Experience simply modifies neuronal expression and brings about a different way of experiencing the environment.

All this means is that there is awareness even on the neuronal level. That is, even the single neuron has its own conditions for consciousness. This awareness is based upon biochemical substances present in the synapse which involve memory. Even at the synapse it is still a level of awareness just the same.

Consciousness is not identified with any particular perceptual/cognitive functions such as a discrimination response to a stimulus, perception, memory or any of the higher mental processes like problem-solving. These responses take place outside of conscious awareness. Consciousness, though, is an experiential feature that may accompany these process.

Consciousness as simply defined as a state of awareness implies that since the neuron does have a certain awareness it also has consciousness.

Thus consciousness stretches deeply into the brain where every neuron's consciousness combines in order to create the total consciousness of the individual.

Reality is perceived through consciousness. Different states of awareness are implied in the term consciousness. Hence, our whole experience is created by our consciousness. This makes our experience a product of the experience of each and every neuron in our nervous system.

As human beings we can learn a myriad of things. From simple tasks such as grasping a glass to the more complex processes such as flying an airplane, we can learn what to do and how to do it. The lower animals do not have the capacity to learn as much or as quickly as humans. They have to rely on other procedures which will assist them in adjusting to and dealing with their environment. The major mode of adjustment the lower animals have is that of instinct. Instinct is a goal-directed type of behavior which has the survival of the species at its core. In the lower animals when the instinctive behaviors of the species are activated the organism would follow it through to completion.

Humans appear to have very few instinctive mechanisms. They appear to be driven mainly by their needs whether these needs be physiological or psychological. Human instinctive mechanisms appear to be abandoned a short time after birth. Apparently nature promotes the ability to learn and to pass that learning on over instinct in humans.

Learning is thought of as an alternative to instinct. Innately guided learning is found at all levels of mental complexity in the animal kingdom. It is believed that the ability to learn is the hallmark of intelligence. On investigation we are led to conclude that learning involves conscious decisions such as what and when to learn. Many researchers have found that a sharp distinction between instinct and learning seems to not exist.

A lot of animal learning is guided by learning programs. Human behavior cannot be explained as simple learning programs. For example, how can the human imagine a solution prior to exploring the situation physically? How also can we imagine the construction of an object from different angles with a minimum of visual data? The process of cognitive trial-and-error and insight learning come closer to the intuitive sense of what intelligence is more so than simply programmed learning. Cognitive trial-and-error requires the ability to recall and combine separate bits of learned information to form new solutions. Insight learning is the forming of unique and different solutions using present available data. Both processes involve what is called map formation. The ability to form maps is not exclusively a human property. The ability to form abstract concepts and categories is.

We cannot discuss learning without also discussing memory. Learning embodies neurological activity. Learning involves more than the accumulation of knowledge and its storage in the nervous system. It also involves the acquisition of memory and its subsequent retrieval or recall.

For a message to go from neuron to neuron neurotransmitters are released at the synapse. The neurotransmitters fit into specific receptors causing channels to open up in the next neuron. This passes the information on. Any mechanism or biochemical that makes a neuron more or less likely to fire plays a role in learning and memory. The changes in the nervous system responsible for memory are assumed to be at the synapses. It is in the synapses where the neurochemicals for the learning experience are held. This insures that the neuron will fire when stimulated.

Remember that the neurons do not react in a step-by-step fashion. Their reacting is in a rising and falling of cellular activities such as biochemical changes. This has been described as a grand convergence of electrical and biochemical events. If perfectly timed it produces enormous neural harmony.

Learning involves a modification in the characteristics of neurotransmitter systems. Other chemical processes along with preexisting neurons and their interconnections with other neurons suggest "hard-wired" nerve networks which change with experience.

Whenever we speak of learning we tend to think it is a single process. We never consider that there are different types of learning and that these types of learning are dependent upon what is being done. To begin with, there are two basic categories of learning. The first is *Nonassociative Learning*. Nonassociative Learning results from experience with a single type of event. For example, in the neuron an increase in response after stimulation creates habituation and sensitization. Second, is *Associative Learning*. This category of learning is caused by the union of two or more events. At the most basic level, associative learning concerns the causal relations between events occurring in the organism's environment. Quite a bit of learning both human and animal is associative.

There is a second system of learning. Aside from and independent of the limbic system's circuits, a different kind of learning is produced. This is from the memories stored through the limbic circuits. This is called *Habit Learning*. Habit learning, itself, may be a primitive type of learning. Habit Learning is noncognitive and not founded on knowledge or memories but on automatic connections between stimuli (S) and responses (R). It is very reminiscent of the automatic S-R bonds of the behaviorists. The limbic system circuits of the brain are an evolutionarily ancient part where habit formation may be located.

The limbic system is the seat of both memory and emotion. Emotion is actually a gate or censor for what is stored. Our moods exert a powerful influence on what we remember. There is a link between stress and the biochemical events in the brain that underlie learning and memory. The limbic system's neurons are loaded with steroid hormone receptors and prolonged stress exposes the receptors to steroids killing some of the cells and destroying the feedback circuits which normally help to turn off the stress.

Stress can enhance some modes of learning. For example, we learn survival skills best when we are alert, attentive and stimulated by the experience. And extreme arousal imbeds the experience into the nervous system. Emotional trauma is extreme arousal that is imbedded deeply into the memory. With the human inclination for generalization there is a strong tendency to assume a singular experience is something that is related to many aspects of life.

All human learning is based on sets of information, or what are called *Constellations of Associations*. In associative learning, different pieces of information are received by the nervous system and their perceived relationship affects the organism's subsequent behavior. Humans have the capacity to construct whole sets of associations. Whenever a relationship is perceived and associations made we have a generalization.

Human beings have the great capacity to (over) generalize from one situation to another. This is not because we cannot tell the difference between the two but with generalization it is assumed that both instances most likely belong to the same set of situations. As such they have the same consequences or outcomes as well. It is these assumed outcomes we are reacting to.

The brain is mainly a parallel information processing system. It is a system with many independent processors doing many things at once. Consequently, the brain operates differently than the computer. The computer processes information in series and at high speed. This means that computer processing is step-by- step. Only after one process is completed does another begin. The parallel processing of the human brain is due to the myriad of dendritic interconnections among the neurons. With this type of construction there is little, if any, series processing going on in the brain.

One of the most important concepts to come out of recent research is the *Essential Memory Trace Circuit*. Left in the particular region after an experience is the essential memory trace. The essential memory trace is described as the neuronal mechanism of adaptability that is necessary and sufficient to store the memory in question. The memory trace is a hypothesized neurologic change which apparently occurs when anything is learned. It is assumed to account for the retention of learned material. It is the neural circuitry from the receptors to the effectors that is necessary and suitable for learning and memory in a given situation. An essential memory trace circuit is a neural pathway which is created in the learning situation and which becomes habituated and sensitized during the learning process.

The collection of neural changes that represent memory is called an *engram*. The engram is an imaginary mediating factor that accounts for retention and it is thought to be a permanent change in the neurons.

To analyze the biophysical mechanisms which form memory traces it is necessary to localize memory traces. Memory trace circuits and memory traces are localized rather than distributed. Localized includes multiple-sites, and within-site traces can still be distributed among neural elements. Essential memory traces are localized to sensory relay nuclei below the level of the thalamus, motor nuclei or reflex pathways.

One of the definitions of memory is that it is *the totality of all of the past experiences which we can remember*. The foundation of our humanity and the basis of our intellect, ideas and discoveries is our memory. The word memory is a catch-all word for a range of processes the brain uses to transpose experience in reality into a series of biochemical and mental elements.

Memory is actually a series of molecular events which begin as sensory impressions. Ultimately they are recorded in the changes stored in the neurons and in synaptic morphology.

Memory is stored in the same neural system that participates in the processing of the information to be learned. For example, the visual system in the inferotemporal cortex, the last in a sequence of visual pattern analyzing mechanisms, is not only a higher order processing region, but holds the visual memories that result from the processing.

Our brain is organized so that separate regions of the neocortex simultaneously carry out computations on specific features or dimensions of the external world. The information storage is tied to distinct processing areas engaged in the learning. The memory is then stored in the areas involved in the processing. Consequently, the more systems you can get involved in the processing of information, the better chance you have of retaining and recalling the information when necessary. The reason being that you have more cues to use to recall the information. The more cues you have, the more processing areas you will engage and the more distinct the memory.

The brain has organized its memory functions around fundamentally different information storage systems. This notion accepts the concepts of both conscious and unconscious memory. The idea of both a conscious and unconscious memory gives us an understanding of the reason we will behave in different ways even in similar circumstances. With an unconscious memory we can see outcomes to events which we would not see consciously. Many of our reactions to the situations tend to be based upon what we had unconsciously perceived in a situation.

Memories are not fixed at the moment of learning. They continue to consolidate or stabilize over time. Consolidation can proceed for as long as several years. During this time the memory depends on the character of the neural systems. Memory consolidation is neither an automatic process with a fixed lifetime or a process determined entirely at the time of the learning. Consolidation best refers to an assumed process of reorganization within the images in the stored information. This continues as long as the information is not being forgotten.

Consolidation is affected by rehearsal and subsequent memory storage events. These events may influence the fate of recent and unconsolidated memories by remodeling the neural circuitry underlying the original representation. Neural assemblies representing stored information could continually reorganize as they adapt to new information. The process of memory storage and consolidation may be competitive, in the same way that competition among axons occurs in the developing nervous system. Any changes in synaptic strength are believed to be the basis for short- and long-term memory.

Combined adaptability is an important form of synaptic change. This occurs when there is activation of a neuron or neural pathway at the approximate time as a second neural pathway. This induces changes in the synaptic efficiency that is not observed when some pathways not adjacent to each other are activated.

Memories are probably not stored exclusively or even mainly in the circuits themselves but most likely in the same areas of the cortex where the sensory impressions take shape (e.g. visual memory is stored in the occipital lobe). Subcortical memory circuits must engage in a kind of feedback with the cortex, after, a processed sensory stimulus activates emotional and memory consolidation circuits in the brain. These memory circuits must playback on the specific sensory area that the feedback presumably strengthens. Perhaps storing the neural representation of the sensory event which just took place. The neural representation itself probably takes the form of an assembly of neurons interconnected in a certain way.

The formation of memory is thought to take this pattern: In *Sensory Information Storage* (SIS) the environmental stimulus triggers the sense organ. This stimulates a neuronal reaction which causes a biochemical release from the forebrain into the sensory area in the brain activating the subcortical memory circuits. **(Figure 2-1)** The stimulus then initiates a series of cellular steps that modifies the synapses in the sensory tissue. This strengthens neural connections and transforms sensory perceptions into a physical memory trace. Consequently, from the simple process of the release of biochemicals the appropriate systems are activated and the memory is created.

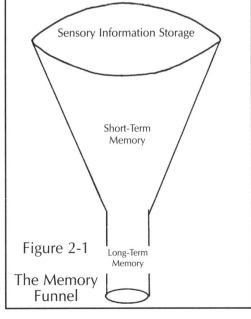

Figure 2-1

The Memory Funnel

Sensory Information Storage

Short-Term Memory

Long-Term Memory

There are two phases seen in memory formation. In the *Initial Phase of Memory Formation*, memories can be altered by subsequent treatments. The hippocampus in the limbic system is necessary for initial memory storage as well as for storage for a limited time and after the learning or during the consolidation of the learned information. As time passes, the role of the hippocampus in memory diminishes. A more permanent memory gradually develops quite independently of the hippocampus. This is most likely in the neocortex. In the *Later Phase of Memory Formation*, memories are relatively permanent. We know that the brain is the processor of sensory information. Neurons in the pathways have "windows" on to the sensory world. As an experience goes on the neurons become progressively broader in both their spatial extent and the complexity of the information which they will admit. The cells learn to respond to progressively more of an object's physical properties.

In order to understand the limits of human information processing we need to distinguish between the two different kinds of memory. First kind of memory is *Long-Term Memory* (LTM). Long-Term Memory is the one feature of our memory system that is relatively permanent. Whenever most people are discussing memory they are generally referring to Long-Term Memory. Whenever information is directed into long-term storage it is usually there for a lifetime. As with any other aspect of learning, long-term memory involves chemical changes at the synapses of the neurons. Long-term memory presumably stores knowledge about grammar and word meanings along with everything else known by the individual. It is essentially infinite and long-lasting in capacity. This is probably due to molecular changes at the neural level.

Long-term memory is seen to take place in the synapses. The odds tend to favor the receiving neuron as the site of the change. It is here at the synapse where the signal carried by neurotransmitter "packets" or "quarks" is released. The synapse is strengthened in two ways: first, the sending neuron could release more packets of neurotransmitters; and second, the receiving neuron might become more sensitive thus admitting a larger flow of ions in response to the same amount of neurotransmitter. If the sending cell would increase the amount of neurotransmitter, it seems that a significant change occurs in the sending neuron.

The second kind of memory is *Short-Term Memory* (STM). This is the realm of memory that the input must pass through prior to going into LTM. STM consists of a set of things to which we are attending at a given time. Presumably it is where we store the words we read or hear while trying to decode them. Its contents are highly transitory; fading almost as soon as our attention shifts. STM holds only a handful of items at a time. Its capacity is no more than about 7±2 items (chunks or bits of data) at a time.

The human brain is made for learning and exploration. It is made up of neurons which actually grow and mature creating more potentialities and abilities. The gathering of information, the learning of new things, and the dissemination of learned experience are natural functions of the human brain.

In order to learn, the brain goes through a simple process. First, when confronted by a situation, a problem to solve, or so forth, it comes up with an approach based generally upon past experience. If the approach succeeds, instructions are sent to the memory to use the same approach in similar situations (generalization). If it fails, it searches through its reasoning or computations to pinpoint the error. Then it adjusts the faulty part of the program in order to bring correct results the next time.

In order for intelligence to exist in an entity there are certain requirements which must be met. First and foremost, it is necessary for the organism to have a good-sized memory. You will remember since the human brain has a stable set of neurons and a relatively stable neuro-chemical structure the memory tends to be quite large. This large-sized memory has wiring to permit the circuits to be changed through experiences. This occurs through the growth of dendrites with the learning experiences. When the entity has greater and richer experiences, this increases the potential for intelligence. Having a series of instinctive reflexive reactions greatly limits the intelligence of an organism. The ability to learn and to project that learning enhances it.

The brain-computer comparison is really not a suitable comparison. The brain with its neurons beats out computers with its silicon memory chips even though the computer operates about 1 million times faster. The secret is in the wiring. Neurons do millions and billions of operations simultaneously. Computers are still based on serial or step-by-step processing. This essentially is set up with a central processing unit, a memory bank and a data channel connecting it all together.

Human learning begins before birth. By finding at which period during gestation different types of learning can occur we can gain a new understanding of the functional organization of the brain before birth. It has been seen that auditory preferences after birth are influenced by what is heard before birth. That is, prenatal auditory experience is sufficient to influence postnatal auditory preferences. Research has shown that fetuses are capable of learning and can express their learned responses in utero. After birth babies respond to the environment from the first day of postnatal life. They can discriminate between objects that they see and they can recognize and respond to the mother's voice.

There is a sudden skill mastery in children from two-and-a-half to three years of age. This is the realization that an object can be understood both as the thing itself and as a symbol of something else. Symbolization is a hallmark of human cognition. One of the most important symbolization functions is the use of language. Once language becomes the primary means of communication the "map" and the "territory" become the same thing.

Scientific psychology began in the mid- to late 1800s. These early researchers assumed the mind was able to observe its own inner workings through the process of introspection. Introspection is an attempt to analyze percepts, memories and thoughts, reducing them to elementary sensations, images and feelings. This research found one's mental life was not just limited to conscious experience. Some researchers found that conscious perception was a product of unconscious influences based on an individual's knowledge of the world and past experiences. This promoted the idea that our conscious mental life was determined by unconscious ideas, impulses and emotions as well as learned defense mechanisms. Consequently, a *Cognitive Unconscious* appeared to exist. The cognitive unconscious consists of mental structures and processes operating outside of phenomenal awareness which influence conscious experience, thought, and action.

The cognitive unconscious encompasses a very large portion of our mental life. A good deal of mental activity is automatic and unconscious. Although we have conscious access to the products of these mental processes, we have no conscious access to their operations.

In order to deal with these unconscious processes, a new theory has been proposed. In this theory, the mind consists of a number of innate specialty-specific cognitive modules or processors. They control activities such as language and visual perception. These are all hard-wired into the nervous system and operate outside of conscious awareness and voluntary control. Other cognitive procedures appear to be acquired via experience. Skills which are not innate can become routinized or habituated through practice, and their operations can be shifted into the unconscious.

Automatic processes are inevitably engaged by triggering specific stimulus inputs. This occurs regardless of any intent on the subject's part. These processes may consume little or no attentional resources but are motivational regardless.

The fundamental premise of cognitive psychology is that the amount of attention that is able to be distributed to various activities is limited. This produces a kind of "bottleneck" in information processing. If deliberate demands exceed designed resources, the tasks will interfere with each other. Routine processes (habit patterns) exhaust little or none of this intended capacity.

There are some negative consequences to automatic processing. For a memory to be memorable, it depends largely on the amount and type of focused cognitive activity devoted to the event at the time of the perception. The more input directed to the perception at the time of the experience the more cues are available for future recall. The more cues available, the easier the recall.

Psychokinesiology is the most efficient and probably most effective way of getting into the unconscious and changing neurological responding. Since learning takes place in the nervous system what Pk does is stimulates the experiences on the *unconscious* level causing circuits of neurons to respond in accelerated ways. Since there is no time in the unconscious this can be done. Research has found that the brain itself does not know the difference between a physical or imagined event so, as you instruct your client's unconscious to think of a particular experience, this change is done amazingly quickly. How it is done is through two processes. The first process is that of emotions and memory having a connection. The second process is that of generalization. There is a simple psychotherapeutic technique for finding the probable basis for a problematic behavior. Have your client think of a particular situation where (s)he did not act as effectively as possible. Make sure that the emotions are experienced as fully as possible. Then using the emotions as a cue have your client go back to the time before when those same emotions were experienced. Then link it to the time before that; and the time before that; and so on until (s)he goes back as far as possible. This linking can bring your client back to a time that may have been the *Time of Origin*. This is a conscious linking process.

With Psychokinesiology you are asking the unconscious if the problem state existed during a particular time period. Unlike a conscious linking process the *Time Reversal* in the unconscious is not bound by any other emotions (e.g. fear).

Consequently, the response that you will be getting will be based on the habit pattern developed from the original experience. Then, when you perform *Resource Realigning* you are readjusting the original emotional reactions so that your client can have more choices available. This increased choice responding comes from the fact that the layered emotions that accompany problem states have been corrected from the very base level.

The brain learns instantly and can remember for a lifetime whatever experiences have been impressed upon it. Psychokinesiology makes learning quick and easy. Since all learning is neurological and biochemical, adjusting the neural activity creates new learning pathways enhancing the generalizations. One of the implications of Pk is that it works outside of the emotions which appear to hold the problem state in place. If this is true then a *Resource Realigning* pulls out the keystone of the behavioral complex forcing the collapse, or rather a *reintegration* of the structure and building a new structure at the same time.

CHAPTER 3

UNDERSTANDING EMOTIONS

Emotions can be seen in the most basic sense as the common experiences of fear, anger, sadness, joy, and disgust. Contentment, satisfaction, contempt, disappointment and so forth are among these as well. We can also include basic sensations such as pleasure, pain, the physiological drives such as hunger, thirst, sleep and sex and subjective experiences such as awe, bliss, inspiration, and other states of consciousness.

Emotions are a two-way street. In one direction we have the perception being experienced. In the other is the bodily response including the biochemical changes occurring in and around the neuron. When emotions are expressed, that is, when the biochemicals of the specific emotion are clear, all of the systems of the body are unified in a discernible expression. When emotions are repressed, denied, and not allowed full expression, this responding is stopped. The biochemicals that contribute to our feelings and creation of wholeness will not have a voice. Remember, it is these biochemicals that run both our body and our behavior.

Repressed emotions and traumas are stored in different areas of the body. This storing is done through the biochemicals (neuropeptides, etc.) which are left after an experience. These biochemical left-overs keep the newly created neural pathways amplified and prepared to respond should a similar experience be reencountered. They also affect the part of the body where the experience is stored preventing our ability to respond fully and appropriately in other situations.

One of the key elements controlling the expression of our emotions is that most of us do not have a handle on true emotional responding.

Most of our emotional expression has been suppressed, regulated, controlled, and manipulated by the time we reach adulthood. Consequently, getting to the actual emotional feeling becomes rather difficult. The main reason is that the true emotion is hidden under layer upon layer of misrepresented feelings.

Our emotional reactions begin in utero. Whatever the mother feels the fetus feels. The experience is remembered and associations are made postnatally to the experience. One of the most important aspects of a person's emotional development is the mother's personality. This has a great deal of influence in shaping the child's basic emotional reactions. The thoughts, feelings and experiences of the mother are part of the repertoire of the child outside of the womb. The mother's diet, illnesses during pregnancy and any drugs that may have been taken will likewise influence how the individual will later respond and cope. Researchers have also found that sound and noise affect the developing fetus. Loud noises, the mother's and father's voice and music will all cause reactions. It is interesting to find that the favorite music of the fetus is from the Classical period, especially Mozart and Vivaldi. Beethoven is too loud and boisterous, rap, heavy metal and even gospel music cause adverse reactions. In order to insure better emotional and intellectual development it is important that the parents talk to the fetus. This insures bonding for both the mother and father with the child. Researchers have seen that schizophrenics had little attention given to them in utero.

The fetus knows much more than had been previously assumed. The rudiments of language are already pre-wired in the human brain so a basic understanding of the syntax and construction of language already exist. Essential reflex reactions are present in the fetus by the fifth week. By the twenty-fourth week the fetus is able to hear. By the third trimester it has accumulated memories. By this time also the personality and character predispositions are in place ready to be activated outside of the womb.

The birth experience and the experiences after birth will strongly affect the child. The birth experience is rather traumatic. It is quite a shock going from the warm uterus to the cold outside. What happens at the birth can affect the emotional reactions of the emerging individual. Researchers have found that there are birth memories. These memories can be either conscious or unconscious. They may come in some symbolic form or in vague representations or recurring statements or patterns in life. Problems at the birth experience (e.g. Cesarean, breech, anoxia) have been known to be projected into other aspects of life such as in relationships or accomplishment of goals. Therapists have even found that the circumcision experience has led to sexual problems in some males.

Borne out by experience, our emotions are the most powerful motivators that we human beings have. Many of us think that we have no control over our emotions and that they simply "happen". Emotions and our emotional reactions are based very strongly on previous experience and associations made in that previous experience.

Emotions are complex reactions which consist of a bodily change from the physiological balance. The emotion itself is experienced subjectively as a feeling and this feeling is in turn shown in bodily changes which are in preparation for noticeable external actions.

Emotion is defined as *a state of affect where what we are feeling causes us to be motivated.* Simply put, this means that emotions are based on affect or moods. The peak of activity of both emotion and motivation is when the organism is totally awake and alert. In any other state the reactions will be distorted and incomplete. The word emotion literally means "to move" and consequently whenever an emotion is engaged there is an accompanying motivation. Emotions *do* move us. First of all, through like and dislike, love and hate, emotions will motivate our behavior either toward or away from something. Other emotions such as fear, anger, joy, sadness, and so forth will likewise activate our behavior into a particular direction. Emotions occur when motives are aroused. So we can see that emotions and motivation are consistently recognized as being together.

Traditional research has discussed five basic or primary emotions. These emotions can be seen cross-culturally as well as in the majority of primates. They are: fear, anger, joy, sadness, and disgust. Some researchers include surprise in this list as the sixth emotion. *Fear is a strong emotion that involves the perception of a real danger, an unpleasant agitation and often a desire to hide or escape.* You will see fear accompanied by actual bodily changes which are mostly in the sympathetic nervous system. *Anger is an intense emotional reaction which is summoned by threat, interference, verbal attack, open aggression, or frustration.* It is characterized by an acute reaction of the autonomic nervous system and by open and hidden attack responses. *Joy is a high degree of emotional gladness and exhilaration.* It is experienced when a situation gives one a feeling of being "uplifted" from the mundane state. *Sadness* is *a feeling of sorrowfulness, grief and somberness.* We usually encounter sadness whenever there is a loss of something to which we had an emotional attachment. It is a feeling of being downcast and possibly even lonely. *Disgust* is not the feeling when you have "had it up to here." That is usually anger or apathy. Disgust is *a feeling, an attitude or an emotion of repulsion, aversion, withdrawal, loathing, and, possibly even, nausea.* We can come across this emotion whenever we happen along a very unappealing situation. That feeling of revulsion and nausea you feel is actually disgust. Finally there is *Surprise.* Surprise is *the astonishment experienced when one comes upon a situation unawares or unexpectedly.* This, unlike the other emotions, can be either a positive or a negative experience. From these basic emotions all of the other emotions are built.

Every emotional state we have has four basic dimensions. The first is the *intensity of feeling.* From emotion to emotion there will be variations as to the degree of the sensation. Emotions such as anger and fear seem to generate the strongest feelings. The emotion of surprise, for example, will provoke strength according to the situation. Second, each emotion has a *differing level of tension.* Each emotion will give rise to different amounts of activity. This activity depends upon the intensity of the feeling and the situation being experienced. Third, all emotions have a *scale of affective tone.* Remember what we are discussing is that of moods. In other words, emotions have a degree of pleasantness and unpleasantness attached to them. The most pleasant is joy. Surprise can be either pleasant or unpleasant. Anger, fear and disgust can all be extremely unpleasant. Finally, all emotions have *differing degrees of complexity.* No matter what the emotion is the experience will be a mixture of thoughts and feelings. Depending upon the physiological associations, the thoughts and feelings can give either a positive or negative experience from the emotional situation.

Human beings have a tendency to *mislabel* the emotions they are experiencing. Many times when a person is feeling simple sadness, unhappiness, boredom, frustration or even apathy it gets labeled as "depression." Depression carries with it a stigma of deep, unrequited unhappiness and misery as well as *specific* behavioral correlations. Often, the individual will automatically take on the features of the label and behave accordingly.

Depression is actually *a feeling of helplessness, hopelessness, inadequacy and extreme dejection, self-depreciation and self-abasement.* These feelings generally occur when there is an experience over which you feel totally unable to control. By being able to see the difference between sadness[1] and depression you will be able to gain some degree of control over your emotions and emotional experience and expression. The problem with mislabeling sadness, for example, as depression is that when you are doing the mislabeling you have no idea consciously what the behavioral correlates for depression are. If you are actually depressed you will have the appropriate behaviors—or should it be said, lack of behaviors.

There are three aspects of an emotion. First is that of the *stimulus* itself. There are arguments as to whether the physiological arousal causes the emotion or whether the emotion and the arousal occur at the same time or whether the emotion produces the physiological changes which prepare the body for flight or fight.

What many researchers are saying occur is that whenever we have an emotional experience we are *labeling* the sensations according to our previous experiences. In other words, we are merely feeling a series of chemical reactions in our body. Whatever we label those chemical reactions to be is what we have been *taught* to label them.

The second aspect of an emotion is the *bodily reaction*. Whenever we experience an emotion we will feel differing levels of physiological arousal. These levels of arousal depend upon the stimulus and the interpretation of the stimulus and the potential outcomes of that stimulus. Emotions also produce specific facial as well as bodily gestures and stances. In this way the emotions can be judged by others.

The final aspect of an emotion is the *mood* or the *feeling* that accompanies it. Each emotion is recognized by the accompanying feeling state being experienced and expressed.

There are primarily two ways that emotions are classified. The first and easiest way is through *pleasantness or unpleasantness*. An emotion either feels good or it does not. From this we say that the emotion is either "good" or "bad." Good and bad are value judgments. It would be better to look at a pleasant or unpleasant emotion as either *appropriate*

---

[1] Sadness, you will notice, has varying degrees. Thus it can be quite easy to mistake sadness for depression.

or *inappropriate* for the situation. Surprisingly, even a so-called "good emotion" can be inappropriate for certain situations. For example acting happily in a potentially disruptive experience will not endear you to any of the people involved. Keeping a "cool head" is more appropriate and realistic.

The second way to classify an emotion is through the *physiological features of that emotion.* Here we are talking about the biochemicals and hormones which the emotion produces. The beta-endorphins have been identified as the neuropeptides of the greatest importance. These, as well as fifty or sixty other specific chemicals including epinephrine have a very strong influence over our moods.

The neuropeptides bring us to a state of consciousness and alter those states. The receptors for neuropeptides, again, are in both the brain *and* the body. The neuropeptides provide a basis for emotions. It may also be that each neuropeptide influences information processing uniquely when occupying the receptors at the nodal points with the brain and the body. If this is true, then each neuropeptide may evoke a unique "tone" that is equivalent to a mood state. Emotions, then, are included in and experienced by not only the brain but throughout the body.

We must remember that the right hemisphere of the brain appears to be more closely aligned to our emotional life. The right side also seems to be responsible for our artistic and musical abilities as well as the comprehension of wholeness. Recall also that the limbic system straddling the inner portions of the brain and above the lower brain centers is considered the seat of our most basic emotional reactions and our emotions are mediated by the limbic system. The limbic system has been seen to be a focal point of receptors for neuropeptides. The receptors for the different biochemicals are not only in the limbic system, specifically in the amygdala and hypothalamus, but throughout the body in nodal points, or "hot spots." These hot spots are anatomically located at places that receive a lot of emotional modulation. The limbic system is highly enriched with emotional receptors. The receptors in this system are forty-times higher than in any other areas of the brain. The "hot spots" correspond to specific cellular groups identified as those mediating such processes as sexual behavior, appetite, and thirst.

Our emotions are messengers that link the major systems of the body into one unit. They have both physical and material substance as biochemical signals that translate information into physical reality.

Remember, what is coming in from the outside are physical *signals*. It is the biochemical signals which turn the physical signals into experience. Emotions are at the bridge between matter and mind ebbing and flowing between the two and influencing both. When emotions are positively expressed, when the biochemicals underlying the emotions are flowing freely, all bodily systems are united in a wholeness. When emotions are repressed, denied, not allowed to be what they are to be, the pathways become blocked. Consequently, the biochemicals that motivate our behavior are restricted causing us to feel ill-at-ease and uncomfortable.

Two emotions which are often confused are fear and anxiety. Fear is one of the primary emotions. It involves the perception of danger, an unpleasant situation and often the desire to run and hide. Therefore, there is a source for the fear. Fear appears to be a reflexive reaction for there are several innate fears in just about all mammals.

Fear has a specific stimulus as well as a maturational component. That is, it can change with age or over a period of time. This means we may lose the fear of a *specific* thing. Remember that the process of generalization expands the responses so that the response can occur with something that is *unrelated* to the original stimulus. Hence, what we can have is an overlying fear that has nothing to do with the original stimulus. In infants, fear is aroused by a sudden or strange stimulus. Later, it is aroused by threats of harm. That harm need not be physical harm either. Fear can be induced by threats of the unknown. Some religions have threatened their followers (and those whom they would proselytize) with condemnation after death if they would not follow their teachings, tenets, their dogma and their laws. It is interesting that even Augustine of Hippo (St. Augustine, 354-430) commented that in order to control the masses, the fear motive had to be induced. It works.

Anxiety is part of the human condition. Because it has no source it is largely learned. Anxiety disorders are the most common health problem in the United States. Anxiety, though, is closely related to fear. It is only the *content* that changes. *Anxiety* is *a general nervous system response that arouses the body to cope with a **perceived** danger.*[2] (You will note the word, *perceived)*. Anxiety involves not a direct threat to one's existence but a perception of *possible* harm. There is no source for

---

[2] The anxiety that is being discussed here is not clinical anxiety which is caused by biochemical interactions.

this fear oriented response. It is that something *may* happen and you do not know what or when. At times, anxiety disorders can be severe enough that they can alter the quality of your life or interfere with your ability to function appropriately in the society. This is when psychological intervention is needed.

Anxiety is characterized by a sense of *vulnerability*. Some of the psychological dangers which are perceived by those who are anxious are humiliation, disapproval, rejection, abandonment, and exposure of personal weaknesses. Some physiological impressions which can bring about anxiety are worries that the sensations being experienced mean mental illness, disease, heart attack, and so forth. Anxiety may reflect the perception of a real danger. Mostly, anxiety is a dysfunction of the mind/body link.

Anxiety gets much of its strength from perfectionism. This comes from the belief that one *must never* be anxious, sad or angry. The perfectionist believes that (s)he must be in perfect control of emotions at all times. Consequently, the anxious individual will be in a constant state of apprehension because of the fear of making a mistake and appearing to be imperfect. This is a highly improbable task so the perfectionist is never satisfied. This makes him/her even more anxious.

Aggression is *an attack or hostile action. At one extreme it may take any form from physical assault to gentle verbal criticism at the other extreme*. This type of behavior may be directed at any thing or person, including oneself. From this definition you can see that aggression need not be direct physical confrontation. It can be, what is termed, passive aggression. This can be seen as directed toward oneself by "setting yourself up" for disappointment, unhappiness, and frustration. It can even be seen in stubbornness.

Several basic psychological causes for aggression have been found. If an adult had received very harsh punishment as a child, that can lead to aggressive behaviors. Likewise, if there was a home life which was violent, aggressive behavior is generally the result. The reason for this is that these are the conditions under which the individual has been raised and, consequently, the individual is familiar with these behaviors. Both of these home atmospheres can promote and foster aggressive reactions in a child. This comes mainly from the modeling of the familiar behavior with reinforcement for that modeling. In these situations, the child knows no better and feels that direct aggression is acceptable. Research has shown that the viewing of violence tends to promote violent behaviors in the viewer. Children become more prone to violence by watching it on television.[3] In attempting to solve problems through violence researchers have seen that biochemically, emotional self-stimulation can alter serotonin levels. This triggers the accompanying emotional changes as well as actually being physically violent. Has that stopped the television industry from producing television shows that contain violence? The answer is, of course, in the negative. All they tell the parents is to be careful what the child watches on television. If the child is there watching the same "adult" television shows as the parent, how can that be controlled? We must also consider that there are parents who see television as an "electronic baby-sitter" and it does not matter if they are home or not. The child is free to watch whatever it wants. Further, there is some speculation that the violence seen on the evening news programs has a kind of desensitizing effect on people. From watching the violence as shown on the news the child comes to view violent activities from a disassociated point of view. Violent actions become something done "out there" by someone else. This occurs whether the individual is sitting and watching television, viewing a violent encounter out the window, actually performing a violent act, or being involved in a religio-philosophical viewpoint that advocates "love" with underlying violent tendencies. For example, religious fanaticism is a form of violence. It has been seen to be linked to lowered levels of biochemical inhibitors. This means that the violent tendencies proceed unchecked by the biological factors. This result came after many years of controversy and research.

The type and amount of aggression is situational. It depends on what is acceptable and safe at a particular time. In essence, much of our aggression depends on our early training. Researchers have found that extreme aggression runs in families.

By now you are probably thinking the only thing that can cause aggressive behavior is one's conditioning and early childhood training. There are also physiological links. Researchers have found that extremely impulsive people of both sexes have low levels of certain biochemi-

[3] In the earlier studies of violence and television it was not discussed if the home environment of the children in the studies was physically and/or psychologically abusive as well.

cals (e.g. 5-HIAA which inhibits neuronal firing). Highly aggressive men have higher levels of testosterone, the male hormone. Testosterone increases the biological intensity of stress, so more adrenaline is released. This produces a state of anxiety and irritability. This state also damages the lining of the blood vessels leading to heart disease. Serotonin, another important biochemical related to many behaviors, has been seen to play a key role in preventing or releasing aggression.

Biology sets the stage for an aggressive act or makes it more likely to occur. It can produce rage or the urge to attack. It cannot dictate whether the attack will take place. That is up to the environment. The environment involves the past and present experience and training and the projection into the future of *possible* outcomes. The actions chosen are those the individual will be motivated to follow due to their *assumed* high probability of occurrence. Most violence in the United States is from people who are chronically aggressive.

You will recall that depression is a feeling of extreme sadness, hopelessness, inadequacy, and helplessness. Just like the word implies, you would feel like something was pushing down on you (depress - to press down). Depression is seen in two forms. First is psychological or reactive depression. *Psychological Depression* is *caused by environmental circumstances*. This can be caused by the loss of a loved one or a perception of abject failure or incompetence. It is usually overcome with the help of a *good* therapist. The second form of depression is clinical or endogenous depression. *Clinical Depression* is *caused by chemical and/or hormonal imbalances*. This may be the result of menopause, premenstrual syndrome (PMS) or some other physiological change. Some forms of clinical depression, such as menopause, can be relieved with time. Others, which are extreme, need the intervention of drugs. An example of how clinical depression works is through a drug addict who is coming down from a high. The drug had taken the place of certain brain chemicals. Due to the lack of these particular biochemicals the brain has to hurry up and remanufacture them. This causes the feelings of depression that accompanies withdrawals.

At one time it was believed that children do not go into depression. This, we know is not the case. Children, as well as adults, suffer from depression and other affective disorders. Many adults with affective disorders showed the first signs during childhood and teenage years. The earlier the onset, the more severe the depression.

There is definite evidence that groups of harmful behaviors accompany depression. The amount of suicide attempts, the percentage of drug abuse, anorexia, bulimia, and juvenile delinquency may be nothing more than methods that young people use to try to cope with depression. There is also fairly solid evidence that suicide is heavily influenced by one's genetics and biology: by their biochemistry.

It is impossible to separate an account of emotion from that of motivation. The emotional arousal of an individual is around a common core of activity that runs through the different emotions such as fear and anger. This common core provides the underlying similarity among emotions.

Emotions help us to adjust to a situation at one time and can actually inhibit our adjustment at another. Laughter, which is a social emotion, is reinforcing when other people are present. It helps to keep us free of unhappiness as well as the relieving of tension. In relatively recent research it was found that laughter increases T-cell (the body's natural killer cells) activity as well as beta-endorphin. This promotes a feeling of well-being along with the release of tension. At the wrong time laughter can prevent you from seeing the reality of a situation and of adjusting appropriately to it.

Strong emotional states, such as anger are disruptive and debilitating and tend to increase your ability to misjudge. This can actually be said about *any* strong emotional state. Even a "positive" emotional state such as joy can actually restrict your ability to judge a situation appropriately. A well-balanced emotional reaction will be an asset.

Inappropriate reactions result from *stress* which surpasses our capacity, real or imagined, to withstand stress. Part of our ability to withstand stress is inherited and part is conditioned. Hence, there is an interaction of nature and nurture.

Essentially, there are three factors that appear to determine our ability to tolerate stress. The first of the factors are *biological* factors. This component deals with glandular (biochemical) activity and the sensitivity of the autonomic nervous system. Inheritance plays a major role here. The second group of factors are *psychological* factors. Here we must consider the individual's internal standards and the anxiety encountered over the failure to meet those standards. These standards are learned from early childhood conditioning: parental dictates, family patterns, and so on. The third of the factors are *social and cultural factors*. We must not forget that each society sets up standards and norms which must be met and to which we must adhere in order to progress in the society. Many of the standards set up by the family are social norms which are learned and promoted.

The stress response prepares the body for "flight-or-fight." When this occurs our internal stores of *glucose* are mobilized from their storage sites. Blood is diverted from nonessential organs to crucial ones (i.e. the heart, skeletal muscles, and the brain). To aid in the processing of information, our cognition is sharpened, our pain perception is blunted, and the physiological activities of no immediate benefit, such as growth, reproduction, inflammation and digestion are deferred.

From this description you can see why it is that chronic activation of the stress response damages your health by various means. Constant glucose mobilization atrophies healthy tissues and fatigue sets in. The cardiovascular changes promote hypertension, thus damaging the heart, the blood vessels, and the kidneys. The constructive processes such as tissue repair, growth, fertility, and immune functioning are impaired and there is an increased susceptibility to peptic ulcers and anything from colds and flus to the increased possibility of cancer.

Research has also shown *testosterone* levels plummeting in response to stressful situations. The highest levels of testosterone seen in the wild are in the dominant males. Testosterone regulates sexual and aggressive behaviors in the male. From this flooding of the system with stress chemicals and hormones, it is easy to see why stress, and the anxiety associated with it, is a major health problem in the United States. In fact, the anxiety disorders are the number one health problem for women and the number two problem, after drug abuse, for men. There are researchers who believe that, for men especially, drugs and alcohol are masks for anxiety. Men appear to have an aversion to showing any sort of anxiety or stress reaction. Most societies, including the American society, have unwritten mores concerning which emotions men are *supposed* to show and which ones are to be repressed.

Anxiety and fear have similar responses but there is a difference. Fear has a specific source. That is, when you are afraid of something, you have an object which is the focus of your attention. In anxiety there is no object. Anxiety is a fear response to something which is *unknown*. Human beings have a unique ability to take that anxiety and, after something happens assign some sort of cause/effect relationship to it. We will assume that it was a particular occurrence which was the cause of the anxiety. The fact is, the assumed cause probably had nothing to do with the anxiety. This incorrect cause/effect assignment at least has relieved some anxiety...until the next time.

Anxiety always has imbedded within it a sense of vulnerability. Feelings like humiliation, disapproval, rejection, abandonment, and exposure of weakness are products of this sense of vulnerability. Because of these imbedded feelings males do not like to show their anxiety. Being seen as vulnerable seemingly shows a weakness which may be manipulated by another.[4]

There are psychological dangers associated with our anxiety and our sense of vulnerability. Some of these psychological dangers tend to be more associated with women and others with men. Sometimes physical dangers are associated with the anxiety. We will worry needlessly about our health. This can cause us to become somewhat the hypochondriac and run off to see the doctor every other day.[5] From time-to-time anxiety can reflect a real danger. This may be something like the fear of a homicidal relative which may show up in your bedroom some late night. Most often, chronic anxiety is a sign of psychological and emotional dysfunction.

There is a mind/body link in reference to every emotion including anxiety. Where a panic attack leads depends on how you interpret anxiety's symptoms. Fear is basically healthy, adaptive and harmless. It becomes destructive when you begin to fear the fear. Anxiety, on the other hand, tends to be non-appropriate in any situation and limits your ability to act, react and emote in accordance with the situation. Think about it. Whenever you are afraid and have no idea what you are afraid of you will not be acting in any sort of realistic manner. Any choice, any person, anything may bring your worst fears to the forefront.

---

[4] Interesting isn't it? Here the male refuses to show his anxiety because it shows that he's vulnerable but then the anxiety associated with the vulnerability produces further anxiety. In other words, he's anxious about his anxiety.

[5] That is, if we have the insurance plan that permits it.

The thought patterns in anxiety and depression are distinguishable. In depression you feel there is a *certainty* that things *are* horrible. Depression emphasizes the past and it mourns the future *as if* it has already happened. Anxiety foresees a *future* disaster and there is physiological preparation for it just in case. You are not sure anything bad can happen. That does not matter. In anxiety there is a belief that things will *become* horrible and hopeless at any moment. There is nothing like a worst-case scenario for keeping you prepared. Even though there could be a 99.9-percent certainty of no problems, it is that less than 1-percent uncertainty that gives anxiety its edge. With these differences it is interesting to note that most depressed people are also anxious.

As in depression, anxiety is classified into psychological or *reactive* anxiety and clinical or *endogenous* anxiety. Reactive anxiety is the general anxiety and fear of the future and the unknown. Endogenous anxiety is some sort of biochemical reaction usually ending up in an anxiety attack.

Anxiety can have any number of causes. They can range from feelings of guilt, rejection, failure, helplessness and *anger* to the idea that something bad *may* happen. Consequently, the approach you take regarding anxiety reflects the particular viewpoint you see as the basis for the anxiety.

Anxiety is the result of future-oriented concerns. People are rarely afraid for extended time periods of situations in the present. In the future, though, we can predict just about anything and that can be the cause of our anxiety. The two most common anxiety-provoking fears tend to be the fear of rejection and the fear of failure. Following closely behind is the fear of being afraid.

We all know that our experience is biochemically based. From our DNA creating the proteins which eventually become the biochemicals of our basic experience to us modifying and creating our own biochemicals due to our experience, biochemicals are an extremely important part of our total behavioral experience. Drug addiction, alcohol dependency and insanity can be looked at as different facets of the same problem. You will recall that norepinephrine and serotonin are the neurotransmitters involved in depression and depression may be at the bottom of all three of these problems. For the addict, it may be that (s)he learns to use drugs to get the feelings (s)he would ordinarily get naturally from the endorphins. The balance between elation and depression is controlled by our natural morphine system. Some persons may be born with defective systems. Others may be born with a normal system but may have it stunted by the lack of proper psychological stimuli. The proper amount of contact comfort, appropriate nurturance and love during the infant critical period may be what is needed in order to have the necessary stimulation for engaging the system. Whether it is genetic or environmental, the person would not have developed the capacity to feel good about him/herself and would be in constant emotional and psychic pain.

The mind is directed by biochemical phenomena. Neurotransmitters, neuromodulators and neurohormones make certain receptors more or less sensitive. Psychological pain circuitry most likely evolved out of the physical pain circuitry, consequently, there is the morphine release which relieves both physical and psychological pain. The brain changes with experience. It continues to stay changed until new learning is placed upon the neurons involved.

Our experience of the world can be changed by changing our beliefs about the world. As we view the world changes, we see new sides to ourselves and new opportunities come into focus. We will then begin to think, feel, and act differently. The chemistry changes that accompany the new worldview would reorganize the existing chemistry and would stay reorganized.

Behind every thought or feeling is a molecular reaction in the brain. Behind every molecule in this reaction is an enzyme that creates the molecule. Behind every enzyme is a gene. If the gene is defective, the enzyme would be defective. With a defective enzyme this would mean that there would be a defective molecule. If there is a defective molecule there is a defective chemical reaction and, hence, a defective thought and accompanying behavior.

A close association has been observed between genetics and mental and emotional diseases. For example, children of alcoholics and schizophrenics tend to model those same types of behaviors. A factor that seems to have a good deal of importance in the behaviors is that of socioeconomic conditions. This means that you will find a higher incidence of abnormal behaviors reported in lower socioeconomic homes than in higher. This may indicate that these abnormal behaviors may be considered more "normal" in lower socioeconomic households where there is less chance of professional psychological intervention. This is despite the genetic component.

As you know the brain and the mind are different. The brain is a physical object which is made up of hundreds of millions of neurons and the mind is a series of processes within the brain. The questions are: Where is the mind located? Is it in a specific part, or outside of the brain. Could it be both inside and outside of the brain? No matter where it is, since it is a series of processes, how does it function in reference to behavior? Finally, what are the processes which comprise the mind?

First of all, the mind is made up of a large number of little processors or agents. Each agent makes connections between things and keeps lists of what things are useful in what circumstances. All of these processors have specific goals that they, without exception, seek even to the exploitation of the other processors.

All of the impressions that we attribute to "mind" are nothing more than linked ideas, neural images, learned through association. Consequently, the processes involved in making up the mind are interconnected thoughts, beliefs, memories, needs, wants, and so on. It is these processes which come together and influence our behavior as well as the physiological reactions of our body.

For many centuries the Mind/Body Problem plagued philosophers. It had been assumed that humans have one mind and one body. The Mind/Body Problem mostly concerns the problem of understanding the relationship between the physical and metaphysical through the transient, though personally real world of the mind and the elaborate activities of the physical body. Even though there are areas of flexibility in the link between the Mind and the Body, we also assume that there are a set of rules that limit this flexibility.

We are all born with genetic inclinations or predispositions. We all have subtle genetic defects or weaknesses not directly causing problems. This makes us more vulnerable to environmental stressors which cause problems. In virtually every situation, there are environmental triggers which will cause certain predisposed problem behaviors to be aroused. Some of these include: indifferent mothering, bad neighborhoods, dehumanizing social or religious systems, and environmental chemicals. The mind and the brain are so closely interconnected that they can be viewed as virtually one. For every thought there is a molecular reaction and for every molecular reaction there is a thought.

In the construction of the brain nature is extremely thrifty. At every level of the brain every level of evaluation which the brain does is built upon what came before. That is, each experience that we have is evaluated beginning from the lowest levels of brain and mental understanding to the highest.

As we have seen, genetics plays a rather large role in our personality and in many of the traits which we possess. There also appears to be a genetic component to the self as well. There seems to be an innate personality substrate which influences our perception of the world. To this we can add that genetics biases the way we think, feel, and act. Environment forms the direction for that action.

Basic to the understanding of the personality, the self and of your perceived world is the understanding of your *worldview*. The *Worldview provides a sense of meaning for the culture and for everyone that exists in it*. There seems to be a necessity that there be a "fit" between the worldview and the world. Both must be closely equated. Otherwise your worldview will no longer give meaning to your life. Disorientation will be the result. There will be a feeling of meaninglessness in your existence and a lack of connection between life's events. The self will become relativized and you will feel a lack of power to bring about change.

The self's center serves as a key frame of reference that will reconnect us with ourselves, with each other, with nature, and with the cosmos. Both human creativity and consciousness have their source in the self's center. This center is both personal and transpersonal. It is the link between our own personal development and the dynamics of personal change.

Our worldview is always supported by the world we perceive. This is why we can change the world by changing our beliefs about it. Beliefs are not concepts about which we are unable to do anything. Beliefs, like many of our attitudes, can be changed. This is obvious. As a child we believed in things like the Tooth Fairy, or that there was something, usually a monster of some sort, which was living under our bed or in the closet. As we matured we dropped these ideas and took on new ones. Our present existence reflects the beliefs we have about ourself and our world.

The main component of the universe is change. In fact, we could say that just about the only thing that exists in the universe is change. It is necessary that we view ourselves not as separate from the universe but at one with it. We are simply cosmological formations. We are simply aspects of the cosmos wanting to know itself. Our particular contribution to the evolving cosmos is our capacity for change or self-transformation.

As we view the world changes, we see new facets of ourselves and new opportunities come into focus. We begin to think, feel, and act differently. As this happens, the energies of life organize themselves differently in us. We will then look out at the world with a new perspective and we will see a world that we had not seen before.

In order to change our worldview, it is necessary to change how we think about the world and about ourself. In order to do this we must tap into our potentials. Consequently, it is necessary that we strive more directly to achieve some levels of self-actualization, self-awareness, and self-knowledge. It is through a new self-consciousness where the worldview is changed and life's experiences evolve.

CHAPTER 4

THE STRUCTURE OF DISORDER

In order to function well within any environment, it is important to be able to adjust to that environment. Many anthropologists believe that human survival in the many environments of this planet has been promoted due to the ability to adapt to the environment. In order to adapt we must be able to adjust our behaviors so survival is promoted. In adapting we also *change* our environment to suit us and our survival. This increases the potential for survival.

The same thing goes for the human ability to deal with other humans. Humans are gregarious animals. This means that humans have an innate need for companionship with others of their species. This banding together is not just for general companionship. Humans are actually rather frail in comparison with many of the other animals. Consequently, they also need to band together for survival. Since most of this survival today has nothing to do with protection from wild animals attacking, this survival is social, emotional, and psychological survival.

Within any group there will be an assortment of differing behaviors, attitudes and so forth. So, there is also a need to be able to adjust to other's attitudes, behaviors and so on as well as to the environment. Anyone who can do this most efficiently has an optimum chance for survival. The *most compatible relationship* we can have *with the environment involves the ability to satisfy most of our needs and to meet most of the demands, both physical and social,* that *we will encounter*. This, in a nutshell, is what *Adjustment* is all about. Adjustment, essentially, is *a process by which the needs of an organism are fulfilled*. It is the constant action and reaction of the individual self with other individuals and the world or the environment.

One of the human being's most important means of adjusting to the social and experiential environment is through emotions. Emotions can assist in this adjustment or they can hinder it. Emotional disturbances occur when an individual's relationship with his environment is not harmonious. This produces stress. These disturbances and stressful experiences can stem from either internal or external sources. The internal sources can come from biochemical interactions or thinking and interpreting the environment in particular ways. The external sources can be from the weather, the environment itself, or from other persons. Being in such a capacity puts us in the position to be confined and restrained by the emotion producing the stress. Once so restricted we will not be experiencing the most worthwhile aspects of life.

Basically, there are three factors that determine our ability to tolerate stress. The first of these are the *biological factors*. Inheritance plays a major role here. Extending from genetics we can look at glandular (biochemical) activity and the sensitivity of the autonomic nervous system (ANS). The autonomic nervous system determines how we are going to respond to an external stimulus. The more sensitive the ANS the more attentive to the environment the individual. Someone who is hypervigilant, overly attentive, tends to be quite nervous and high-strung. The flight-or-fight response is an autonomic nervous system function.

To understand our general biological roots we need to consider genetics and the problems associated with improper DNA encoding. This can bring about chemical imbalances. These imbalances can stretch all the way from inherited brain dysfunction through to bipolar disorder. The second factor determining the ability to tolerate stress is that of *one's personal judgements*. Here we must consider our internal standards and the anxiety encountered over the failure to meet those standards. The standards we have are all learned from early childhood. Our family is the most important agent of the installation of these standards. Virtually all of our choices are based on our personal judgements of the environment and assumed outcomes in the future. The third set of factors determining the ability to tolerate stress are *social and cultural factors*. In the cultural context each society has unspoken mores which define what is normal behavior and what is not. Once a member of the society crosses the line that person is branded as problematic and may be ostracized. There are times, and history bears this out, when a society is in the midst of a transition of some sort. During this time a person who would ordinarily be considered problematic says what the people want to hear and becomes a social leader. He finds a way of allowing the society to express its inner fears. A scapegoat is set up for his own emotional and the society's problems. Thus far, a social leader of this type never has brought about positive change. It seems that the people listening and adhering to this sort of social leader have personal problems of their own and a scapegoat is what everyone is looking for. We must not forget that each society sets up standards and norms which must be met and adhered to in order for the individual to live in that society. Many of the standards set up by the family ("family values") are the social norms which are learned and promoted.

By far the vast majority of emotional problems have *psychological roots*. That is, an individual *learned* inappropriate emotional and behavioral reactions. This training could have come from early family behavioral patterns, physical and/or psychological abuse and/or lack of appropriate nurturing by parents. In essence, the problematic behavior has its basis in early childhood relationships and training. With maturity this training is adjusted to fit the external experience. Most often it is not disengaged. The behaviors are continued because by the time of adulthood they are part of the individual's personality traits and (s)he is comfortable with them.

If you ask most people what abnormal behavior is they will usually make a statement such as, "It's when someone acts real weird." When questioned further regarding what "weird" means you will most likely hear something like, "You know, when somebody goes around screaming at people who are not there or seeing things that are not there or something like that." The abnormal person is generally considered one who is not simply emotionally troubled but mentally deficient.

For countless millennia there have been two opposing points of view about the cause of emotional disorders. One group saw the supernatural at work producing the problematic behavior. There were two camps in this group. One camp accepted the behavior which was considered strange or unusual as being caused by "demon possession." Whenever a person saw things that no one else saw or talked to people who were not visible it was a demon of some sort. In fact, the cultures who saw demon possession as causing abnormal behaviors even had names for the demons that caused the specific behavior seen in the person. The other camp saw it as being close to God. The reason for the second camp was that when a Pagan priest or priestess prior to prophecy went into an altered state of consciousness and began to prophesy[1] they would babble and act like one who was mentally deficient. Later, in the Judeo-Christian era especially, the mentally deficient, as well as the Pagan oracles, were considered "demon possessed." This idea was most likely promoted because of the consistently reliable accuracy of Pagan oracles and the exceptional inaccuracy of accepted traditional Christian writings and predictions[2]. This accuracy would disenfranchise the Christian priests after a while.

The second viewpoint saw any abnormal behavior as being caused by natural forces both genetic and environmental. Today we see any *Abnormal Behavior* as *behavior which is* generally considered *statistically unusual, strange or undesirable by most people, and a source of unhappiness*. When we consider this type of behavior to be a source of unhappiness we mean that it is a problem for, not only the immediate family but also for the individual performing the behavior. Beyond that, this behavior also poses a problem for both the individual *and* for the society. It is not just the unusualness of the behavior which is the problem for the society. It is also a fact that the society must find some way to take care of the individual performing the abnormal behavior.

Abnormal behaviors are believed by many researchers to result from *stress* which surpasses our *perceived* capacity to withstand stress. You will recall that part of our ability to withstand stress is inherited and part is conditioned. Hence, there is an interaction of nature and nurture involved in abnormality.

We cannot know what is abnormal without having some idea of what is normal. Many times, normality tends to be confused with reality. There are rather large differences between normality and reality. *Normal Behavior* is *behavior that agrees with or conforms to a society's accepted pattern of customs, rules, laws, fears, and taboos*. It is being and acting according to the accepted precepts of a society.

---

[1] For example, the famous Oracle at Delphi or at Ephesis.

[2] See *The Arguments of the Emperor Julian Against the Christians*, Thomas Taylor (Ed.), Hermetic Publishing Co., Chicago, IL, 1932

Reality, on the other hand, is *that part of the universe which is not fantasized*. Reality is the portion of our life that we are paying attention to. It is that which is seen visibly, heard auditorially, felt physically, smelled and tasted. Reality is not what is seen in a dream, whether in the night or the day. It is not what is heard inside of the head and projected to the outside. It is not the "crawling insects" of the drug addict or the schizophrenic. *Reality* is *that which is perceived by the physical senses*.

Normal and *real* may not be the same things. Indeed, often they are not. You will find many religious sects who have their followers performing what they consider "normal" behavior for them, but abnormal for the general society. Adherents must follow their laws and rules. All of which are assumed to make some sort of *supposed* contact with a presumed existing nonphysical entity or energy. So strong can the activities and *suggestions* of the leaders of the group be that the followers will claim to have actually been in contact with whatever it is or to commit suicide to prove their "faith."[3]

Every society has sets of accepted norms and patterns for behavior and everyone that is within that society must follow those behavioral norms and patterns. *A behavior which does not conform to the usual type of behavior that is expected* is labeled as not realistic and called *Abnormal*.

Fantasies are not a form of abnormal behavior. Everyone has a fantasy life of one sort or another. It could be as trivial as getting in the car and driving away for the weekend or punching the boss and getting away with it. Whenever we come to believe that our life is dull and lacks fulfillment and excitement we can become hooked on the "soaps," talk shows, sports on TV, or into fantasy programs such as "Star Trek."[4] These are all types of vicarious living and a fantasy life.

---

[3] Richard Bandler the co-founder of Neuro-Linguistic Programming paraphrased Carl Jung when he said, "When one person claims to see angels and demons and to talk to God he is usually locked up. When a whole group claim the same thing it's called a religion."

[4] The difference between a "Trekker" and a "Trekkie" is that a Trekker puts on a set of pointed ears and *pretends* to be a Vulcan. The Trekkie puts on the ears and *claims to be* a Vulcan.

Fantasies exist. They are made up of dreams, wishes, desires, imaginings, and impulses from the unconscious. They represent the raw, primitive, amoral, egotistic forces in our personality. Fantasy is an entirely *normal* part of the reality of life. A fantasy is, in one instance, creative because of the interesting situations in which we place ourselves. In another instance it is uncreative because it does nothing about making change in our life.

Fantasies can be taken to an extreme as well. They can come to be a form of *escape* or even an *avoidance* of reality. Even the fantasies from television or any other part of the media can do this. Whenever anyone becomes so involved in what is happening on any of the soap operas or the statistics of sports figures or the problems of people on the talk shows that it takes over their life, there are emotional problems which need to be addressed. Any excessive or uncontrolled fantasy becomes a symptom of internal conflicts. When the fantasy is thought to be a reality there are definite problems. In a fantasy you always place yourself in a position where you are the one who has all of the answers, you are in control, you are the peerless individual. When you take these fantasies to be closer to reality than your real life, then they are hiding the feelings of inferiority which may be plaguing you. How many times as a child did you go to see a movie and you become the hero whether it was Superman, Wonder Woman, a cowboy, Batman, Peter Pan or one of the Teenage Mutant Ninja Turtles or Power Rangers? There is nothing really wrong with this. It is when the fantasy is used *in place of reality* that trouble occurs. This behavior we find in psychotics and some extreme neurotics.

The key to understanding emotional disturbance is to look at how an individual handles fear, anxiety, and stress. Anxiety is a general nervous system response that arouses the body to cope with perceived dangers. Anxiety is part of the human condition. In understanding a person's ways of dealing with disturbances nature and nurture interact. Looking at this interaction provides the personal structure in the depth of the individual's ability to cope.

Anxiety disorders can be severe enough to alter the quality of a person's life to the point of actually interfering with the individual's ability to function effectively. Anxiety is always characterized by a sense of vulnerability. Remember, excessive emotional reactions are crippling and can destroy the ability to respond appropriately and effectively in a situation.

It has been found that genetic and environmental factors are roughly equal in determining behavioral responses. The three specific dimensions of the personality; harm avoidance, novelty seeking, and reward dependence, are genetically independent. They have patterns of interaction in their adaptation responses in reference to novel, disturbing and desirable stimuli. The stimulus-response patterns of these three dimensions are characteristic of the three associated brain systems for behavioral inhibition, activation, and maintenance. These systems have predetermined underlying heritable differences in the three personality dimensions.

Biology influences our behavior and behavior affects biology as well. We need to remember that learning changes the genetic structure of the nerve cells within the central nervous system. There is some evidence that this can be passed on to one's offspring.

There is ample evidence that depression can have either a biological or a psychological component. Whether you are depressed because of a biochemical change or due to some environmental factor, you will be reacting with the same behaviors. In the psychological depressive reaction depression is seen in a three-fold pessimistic triad: 1) a negative view of yourself; 2) a negative view of your personal reality, and 3) a negative view of the future. The main causes of psychological depression are: 1) a personal conviction in your own personal deficiencies. The ideas of being a *total failure*, a *miserable sinner*, or could have *accidentally* hurt someone. There are constant thoughts concerning a personal belief in your needing to be punished for doing "bad" things and for being imperfect; 2) self-pity, not having *your* way or not having what *you* want or need to seemingly make you happy; and 3) being upset and angry over the way that people are and the world is. In other words, you are assuming a position that if you get upset over conditions which are out of your control, somehow someone, or maybe even ourself, will be able to do something and immediately right everything.

Due to Freud's theories, depression and other affective disorders and major emotional problems were thought to be exclusive to adults. We know that is not true at all. Children and adolescents suffer from major depression as well. Major affective disorders, including depression and bipolar disorder are seen to exist in young people as well. The difference is how those disorders are being acted out. Adults will behave in ways that are more traditionally seen as being the disorder. Young people, who have not had the experiences that the adults have, will not. Suicide attempts, drug abuse, anorexia or bulimia, juvenile delinquency, including gang or group membership of any sort can be seen as some of the ways that young people act out their emotional problems. Often when this energy is redirected then the problem behaviors will disappear. Suicides, for example, are the third leading killer for adolescents. One of the most important risk factors for suicide is an untreated emotional disorder. The estimates are that at least one-third of all adolescents have an untreated or undiagnosed emotional disorder.

The diagnosing of the affective and emotional disorder in the young person is not easy. The problem is that young people show a more diverse set of symptoms than do adults. It is hard to tell which behaviors are typical rebelliousness and which are the result of depression. As young people develop, boys tend to act out their depressions aggressively. Girls, on the other hand, seem to direct their actions inwardly. It is believed that this has something to do with the different cues which are important in forming a boys self-image verses a girl's self-image during puberty. One important factor in the diagnosis is the family history of affective disorders. There may be a genetic predisposition when depression starts in childhood. In other words, if a youngster has a parent which is bipolar there is a twenty-five percent chance of that youngster being bipolar as an adult. The genetics may merely contribute to the vulnerability to depression and bipolar disorder. What is needed is some psychological, social, or biological factor to bring the problem to the forefront.

Disintegration of a sense of self-esteem is also an important factor in depression. The traumas of the 1960s forced people to turn inward. With the ending years of the 20th century the trauma of an unknown future and the doom-gloom prophecies (both religious and secular) are feeding these fears and creating an intense anxiety producing depression. The generally inward-directed depression becomes outwardly directed toward innocent members of the society. Thus we see an increase in violent acts, self-at-all-cost behaviors, and suicides. This is comparable to the grief process. So, if there is a genetic predisposition, it could easily touch off a disorder.

A nurturing environment can ease genetic tendencies. If we learn enough about the genetics, biochemistry, and social factors which combine to produce a behavior problem, this can help reduce the incidence of the problem.

In the brains of many bipolar individuals nerves have been found leading from the limbic system into parts of the hypothalamus which control hormonal release. What researchers could be seeing is the reduced ability of the body's stress-handling system to adapt being expressed physiologically. So the levels of neurotransmitters do not change as they should. Genetic defects somehow diminish the system's flexibility so that repeated stresses wear it down further. This eventually induces the depression side of the bipolar disorder.

Some interesting research has brought to light certain aspects of brain hemispheric dominance in depression. Research has found that the rate that glucose (sugar) is metabolized in the brain is a good indicator of overall brain activity. In the left frontal lobe especially, during mania the activity is higher than normal and during depression, it is lower than normal. Other researchers have seen that during depression the left frontal cortex is relatively inactive as seen on EEG tracings. In response to any arousing stimuli, there is a less than normal increase in the Galvanic skin response (GSR) of the right hand. Also, when dealing with a cognitive problem, a depressed individual's eyes tend to gaze to the left and down. This indicates a right hemispheric activation. The average individual's eyes gaze to the right. The indication with the eyes to the right is that the left hemisphere, the more logical hemisphere of the brain is being activated. It has also been seen that people with brain damage in the frontal lobes of the left hemisphere are generally depressed, or at least pessimistic. Persons with damage to the right frontal cortex are either emotionally unresponsive or possibly euphoric.

What does this all mean?

The right hemisphere, it is known, has limited language skills in many persons. It is not able to really understand strings of words but can judge the syntax of the sentence. It is able to perceive melodies and analyze nonverbal patterns and, very important here, the right hemisphere cannot contribute to problem solving without the left hemisphere. The right hemisphere reaches solutions through *leaps of insight*: seeing the whole gestalt or relationships not aware to the left hemisphere.

The left hemisphere is specialized for language in the vast majority of people. It is able to interpret actions, moods, and thought processes. It is able to construct theories about these actions and feelings and it tries to bring order and unity to our lives. It has the singular capacity for making causal inferences. The left hemisphere works in a step-by-step, ordered fashion being the expert in problem solving via established methods.

Recall the last time that you, or someone that you knew, were feeling depressed, or even deeply troubled. Trying to speak, to think, to reason, to understand were all quite difficult. These processes are all mainly left hemispheric processes. Every experience had a negative connotation. Everything looked like it was out to increase the problem. Anything anyone said was taken wrong. These processes, being emotional responses, come from the right hemisphere. With the left hemisphere being relatively inactive during depression, the functioning of the right hemisphere would increase. The individual thus affected would make "leaps of insight" which would be highly emotional and totally incorrect for the situation being untempered by any left hemispherical controls. Hence, *depressed persons are right hemisphere active and left hemisphere repressed.*

Human beings do not have to concern themselves with being lower on the food chain as they had when they were skulking around the savannahs in Africa. At that time their main concern was to gather food for themselves and the tribe and keep away from predators such as leopards and lions. It was those predators which gave humans their main anxieties and fears. Today those anxieties and fears have been transferred to relationships: loving, working, and general relationships. Much of the human being's anxieties are based on "what if..." concerns. The danger situations arise primarily from the *interpretation* of the external reality or from some aspect of an objective relationship. In this situation the external experience may signal danger and prompt a fear response thus producing an emotional disturbance. Most of the time it is a person's thoughts, beliefs, and attitudes which create the problem. External situations can evoke overreactions because of the projections that a person places on what is occurring in the environment. This will heighten the sense of danger increasing both fear and anxiety. The main problems come from the perceived locus of control of a situation being "out there" somewhere. We do not have any way of handling it because we are the most insignificant part of it. Most people believe that their emotions lie outside of them and outside of their control. Emotions are an individual's personal response to the environment. The behavior that a person expresses is a byproduct of the emotions that they are feeling at the time. In order to achieve emotional choice you need to know how to select and access the most appropriate emotion for the time and place. It is important to remember that the interpretation that you place on the environmental experience brings the emotion that you will have and the subsequent behavior that you perform.

Those actual and imagined sources of danger, those which are realistic and external and those which are unrealistic and psychological are taken into account with each choice made. Threats to the self-concept, the identity and other personal areas are related to these basic dangers. Consequently, the danger is assumed to be directed to one's self. Quite often we will identify ourself with something, someone or a group. The reason for this being we have a lesser sense of self than is appropriate for effective functioning in our social structure. Once we have made this identification and have incorporated this identification into our emotional and ego structure, it becomes who we are. That is, we no longer are an individual. We are the thing with which we have made the identification. In order to maintain that identification we will take on all of the behaviors, attitudes, values and so forth of the thing. We may even defend our identification to the death if necessary. Without that identification we are nothing.

Not only does this process work with objects, it works with labels. This means that literally anything that you consistently identify yourself with you will become. So, if you state something like, "I am depressed" enough times you will begin to take on the behaviors, attitudes, thought processes of being depressed. Once you have placed your body in the position to assume the stance of a depressed person your body will begin to respond. It will begin to secrete the biochemicals that will bring about the depression. The same goes for any other identification, emotional or otherwise. The constant identification with it can eventually bring about the state.

The stress response prepares the body for "flight-or-fight." When this occurs our internal stores of glucose are mobilized from their storage sites. The blood is also diverted from nonessential organs to crucial ones (i.e. the heart, skeletal muscles, and the brain). To aid in the processing of information, our thinking is sharpened, our pain perception is blunted, and the physiological activities of no immediate benefit, such as growth, reproduction, inflammation, and digestion are suspended.

It is easy to see why chronic activation of the stress response damages your health. By identifying with and assuming a hypertense attitude your whole system can be harmed. The biochemicals promoting the emotional (fear, anger, etc.) response will be continually pumped throughout your body. This can also lead to chronic exhaustion. The constant glucose mobilization atrophies healthy tissues, and fatigue sets in. The cardiovascular changes promote hypertension, thus damaging the heart, the blood vessels, and the kidneys. The constructive processes such as tissue repair, growth, fertility, and immune functioning, are impaired and there is an increased susceptibility to peptic ulcers.

By flooding the system with stress chemicals and hormones, it is easy to see why stress, and the anxiety associated with it, is a major health problem in the United States. As we've seen, anxiety disorders are the number one health problem for women and the number two problem, after drug abuse, for men. Drugs and alcohol most likely are masks for anxiety and their use may be the only way these men feel they have to express their fears. Men, it seems, appear to have an aversion to showing any sort of anxiety or stress reaction. Our society has unwritten mores concerning which emotions men are supposed to show and which ones are to be repressed, how, when, and to whom these emotions are to be expressed.

All emotional disturbances are based unconsciously on perceptions and fantasies which are outside of personal awareness. This means that we are acting upon expectations and assumed outcomes which we are not even conscious of. Remember that the brain is constantly making associations as it experiences the sensations coming into it. These associations are based on literally *all* of its previous learning, projections into the future of possible outcomes, and past choices. From this the brain chooses the most appropriate possibility upon which to react. All of this is instantaneous and automatic. The encoding of the material for personal interpretation is disguised in behaviors, rationalizations, displacement of emotions, emotional misinterpretations and layering, and fantasies. So, what is happening is that the individual is reacting to the encoded material and not the reality. This distorts the incoming and outgoing data leading to the formation of more symptomatic behaviors. These behaviors will keep the individual from realizing what is actually happening on the outside and the environmental experience is distorted and misinterpreted.

Emotional disturbances can arise through either an actually perceived or an imagined danger. Both of them can evoke conscious and unconscious memory responses. These responses will contribute to the client's feelings of vulnerability. Then, due to generalization the present experience is associated with something from the past even though it has nothing whatsoever to do with the original experience.

Traditional psychotherapy seeks to find the basis of the problem state by tracing the sequence of transactions that lead to the emotional disturbance through conscious direction. *Psychokinesiology* does not need the conscious interpretation. Instead of having to deal with any sort of conscious blocks and emotional overreactions Pk does not use personal histories, ego defenses, fantasy-memories, or intrapsychic experience. With Pk you can deal directly with your client's *unconscious* interpretations of his environment. These unconscious interpretations are prime motivators for behaviors and instigators for choices.

Most people accept that these unconscious motivators come from the unconscious mind. Traditionally it has been customary to view the unconscious mind as being associated with the brain. In recent research it has been found that *not only the brain but the body has receptors for the biochemicals of emotion*. The implication is that **the body is the unconscious mind**.[5] As you have already seen, repressed emotions are stored in different parts of the body. There are specific neuropeptides associated with each emotion and certain organs and body parts have the receptors for these specific neuropeptides. Consequently, these certain repressed emotions are stored in specific organs. By accessing particular organs it is possible to get in touch with the emotional energy welled up in it. Once this has been established it is also possible to clear that problematic emotion. This is where *Psychokinesiology* has an advantage. As you will find in succeeding chapters, problematic emotions are accessed by "tuning in to" specific organs. After you have gained access to the organ you can find the precise emotion which has given the problem, get to the *Time of Origin*, find the processes holding it in place, realign it and project the realigning into the future. This projection into the future establishes a link from the present. Like linking the present emotion into the past the *Time Progression* process takes the unconscious into the future. There is no time or space in the unconscious, consequently, the unconscious will react in a different manner because it assumes a different set of rules due to the change. New choices will become available and your emotional expression will be more appropriate for your experience.

5 See *Molecules of Emotion* by Candace Pert, Ph.D.

CHAPTER 5

RAPPORT

The initial and key element in any therapeutic intervention is rapport. Without rapport the chances of being able to assist in the effective change of another person are quite slim. Consequently, the importance of immediate rapport with your client cannot be overstated.

Even before gaining rapport with another, rapport with yourself is paramount. Rapport can be defined as *the establishing of trust, harmony, and cooperation in a relationship*. It is essentially meeting another in his/her model of the world. This acknowledges their current state of consciousness. This acknowledgement intensifies the feedback loop thus increasing your ability to *influence* your client.

In establishing and maintaining rapport, you are essentially making agreements with both the conscious and unconscious mind of your client. This creates an atmosphere of trust and credibility. This atmosphere builds positive expectancies that will increase receptiveness and responsiveness.

When rapport is built-up it allows your client control within the loop. When appropriately performed you can then turn the rapport around and bring your client along with you.

Rapport-building and maintaining techniques can be taught. Some people who have learned how to establish a level of rapport with another can do it *technically* but cannot maintain the rapport consistently through time. This is because something is lacking within them. What is missing is an internal harmony or a rapport within themselves. Once this internal rapport is established, rapport with another is a natural consequence.

Self-rapport is essential prior to being able to effectively maintain rapport with another. Self-rapport is *congruency between your internal and external feeling states and your behavior*. It is an awareness and acceptance of what is going on within yourself *at the present time* so that your self-talk and your behavior are focused to the same end.

Self-rapport is acknowledging and evaluating your own present state. It is the first stage of getting busy with your self. Self-rapport is a tool that is utilized to bring about balance and harmony, first of all within yourself, then in your present experience.

There are two basic stages in the achievement of self-rapport: 1) acknowledging and attending to, or evaluating, your present experience (What am I aware of *right now?*); and 2) creating a balance within yourself. After you have achieved rapport with yourself, you can concentrate on getting rapport with your client. Hence, getting self-rapport is the first step in getting ongoing rapport with your client. Further, with self-rapport when dealing with your client you will not be letting any part of yourself get in the way of helping him/her.

The first step in the process of creating self-rapport is to *observe*. That is, you must pay attention to what is going on inside of yourself. One of the keys is to determine how closely your external behavior matches your internal state. In your self-observations you will need to ask yourself certain questions:

1. What *specifically* am I feeling? What emotions do I *now* have?

Most social scientists categorize five major emotions. The objective here is to get to the *core* emotion. Once there you will be able to tell more clearly if what you are feeling is what you are expressing. Verbalizing your emotion at the time that you are feeling it can increase your awareness of your experience.

2. Do my actions *appropriately* correspond to what I am feeling?

So often when you are feeling one thing you are acting out something else. This is a defensive characteristic of enculturation and socialization. According to the culture you must act specific ways at certain times. But many persons continue the same behaviors outside of the context and it does not work. This is called emotional and psychological aberration. By attending to both your internal and external feelings you are better able to adjust to the external experience with greater flexibility.

3. What in the environment is the same as the previous experiences I have had that seem to be leading to (a) specific outcome(s) and what are the differences?

This is an important question because human beings are creatures of habit. Human beings will tend to repeat the same behaviors over-and-over in spite of the fact that the present environmental stimuli are *weak approximations* of some stimulus that was experienced years ago. So, we will *unconsciously* assume that the same outcome(s) will result. Here also you need to get into the *specific* feeling that you are experiencing.

What you have probably noticed, the most important aspect of observation is congruency. This is true. Without congruency between the internal and external experience your observation will be flawed. Flawed observations mean that you will be seeing only what you *want* to see. You will be making judgements based upon an incomplete picture of the experience. From an incomplete picture assumptions will be made that all experiences of a *similar* type will bring the same outcomes. This is essentially how generalizations are created. Through the processes of deletion and distortion of incoming and outgoing data you encode, decode and react to your world experience.

Knowledge and awareness of what is going on inside is a major step in attending to what is happening on the inside. Having rapport with yourself means you are aware of your inner workings and your outer responses. Establishing and maintaining rapport with yourself means that you are able to understand and direct your own experience. Once in this position you can *choose* the inner experience that you want. You are not getting in your own way of fully experiencing your reality.

Being in self-rapport is getting in touch with what you are feeling and being involved with your experience. You are attending to and cooperatively and congruently working with your self. To do this you must be calibrating to your self-experience. This calibration is the basis for dealing with your feelings.

Self-rapport is the main tool for plugging into other processes. When in self-rapport you will have a feeling of comfortableness, harmony, and balance. You will have a focused and integrated system. In essence, you will be fine-tuning your own ability to deal with your environment.

Self-observation is not self-absorption. To observe yourself does not mean that your attention is focused strictly on your own wants, needs, and desires. It has nothing to do with that. It has to do with *defining* your feelings, behaviors, motivations, and directions. This naturally leads to self-calibration.

The next step in self-rapport is adaptation. This means being aware of what is going on inside *and* outside of yourself. It is having the awareness that what you are feeling and thinking is *congruent* with the way you are acting and what you are saying. Adapting to yourself gives you an awareness of your own inner workings.

In social psychology there is a process referred to as "emotional dishonesty." This is the idea that you will express one feeling while experiencing another. Many of you will recognize this as the Freudian ego defense of reaction formation. There are several major problems with emotional dishonesty/incongruity of feelings:

1. As dishonest as you are with others, that is what you expect from them.
2. It is a cover-up of our true feelings and it is quite uncomfortable.
3. False information is communicated causing inappropriate reactions from others tending to reinforce the incongruity.
4. The feelings that you are not trying to communicate will come out.
5. It is unintentional and, in many instances, on an unconscious level. That is, it is a habit.

When you are incongruent with your inner thoughts and feelings and your outer behavior, expecting your environment to respond any differently than with what you are feeling is totally irrational.

Self-adjustment deals with inner awareness. Before you can be aware of what is happening on the outside you need to have an understanding of what is going on inside. This inner awareness deals with more than just being able to state what primary or core emotion you are feeling at the time. It has to do with other processes such as: motivations (What are you moving toward and what are you moving away from and why?); the focus of your attention (Are you more self- or other-directed?); your focus for decision-making (Are you internally or externally-directed?); whether you are active or passive in life and decision-making; if you tend to see the big picture or the details; whether your beliefs are consistent, incongruous, or a combination of different systems; if your personal rules and beliefs have application to others or not; how you respond to stress; finally, is your behavior directed by needs, pressures, etc. or by options, opportunities, and so on.

Since inner awareness is not taught in most western schools, this skill is lacking to a large degree in the general population. To observe and calibrate your own thoughts and feelings in any meaningful way requires concentration. Some persons have learned certain aspects of self-awareness in specific disciplines to, for example, excel in sports and games, psychotherapy, in some ashrams and religious centers, or simply from self-discovery in their search for meaning in life. Usually these modes of learning concentration and awareness have been motivated by the desire to excel in a particular area. Consequently, learning this skill does not necessarily carry over into other areas of life since the skill was applied to a specific area for a very specific purpose. In other words, the skill is essentially "state specific." Awareness provides a foundation from which to evaluate, or interact with your own internal responses.

One of the keys to self-rapport is *staying in the present*. To develop more self-awareness requires you to be in the here-and-now. Reality is in the present and whenever your mind wanders into the past or the future you are in a mode which is powerless to affect the present. You cannot possibly change the past. All you can do is use the past as a learning experience to help you in decision-making and goal planning for the future. The past is already completed and there is nothing you can do about it. The future is not here yet and all you can do about it is to make plans in the present to achieve your goals. Actually, the only thing that you can really deal with is the present: the here-and-now. Unless your thoughts about the past or future pertain to something that you can act upon in the present, it is simply an escape from the reality of the now; a fantasy. Most psychological problems such as depression are created by thoughts of loss and disappointment related to the past and fear and anxiety about the future.

In order to have awareness of yourself it is necessary to be focused in your present experience both internally and externally. To be in the present does several major things:

1. It eliminates confusion and scattered thinking. It allows you to be solution-oriented engaging many processes of both the left and right hemispheres of your brain. This allows both the analytic processes of the left hemisphere and the integrative processes of the right hemisphere to operate more effectively.

2. It eliminates "stuck" states and repressed emotions. Both "stuck" states and repressed emotions are *in time* processes based on a complex of thoughts and feelings adhering to past experiences acting *as if* they are in the present. You are holding on to something that happened in the past and not releasing it and learning from the experience.

3. It improves self-confidence creating more self-power and enhances your ability to reach and fulfill your goals. This means that you are in control of the present experience and are actively participating in the creation and re-creation of your personal universe.

4. It enhances your intuition. Much of intuition is nothing more than paying attention to trends, directions, and choices that you and others around you have made. This means that you, (a) analyze a situation paying attention to the whole environment, (b) consider past experiences which were similar to the present one and take into account the outcomes received, (c) bring together the past and the present projecting *possible* outcomes, and (d) selecting the best possible course of action. All of this is done somewhat instantaneously. Hence, it seems like it is a "flash of insight" from some unknown source. It is a natural process of being in the present.

5. It eliminates stress and anxiety. You are no longer "stuck" and depressed about the past or anxious and fearful about the future. The past is a learning experience and the future is the result of your choices.

6. It improves clarity of perception. You will see things *as they are* not as you would like them to be or as you want them to be. Again, you are focused neither on the past or the future.

7. It gives you peace of mind freeing your body and spirit. This means that you will be more able to engage your whole system into accomplishing your goals. You will also better understand the difference between what your ego wants and what you really need.

Awareness alone is not going to help you to adjust or achieve self-rapport. The next step to the experience of your present reality is *acceptance*. Acceptance does not necessarily mean that you *like* or agree with the experience. It simply means that you accept your sensory input for what it is—*sensory input!* This is the most basic part of the process of acceptance.

People will sometimes say, "I do not want to feel ____. I want this feeling to go away." These statements demonstrate that the person is not accepting their sensory input. What has happened is that the present sensory input is *assumed* to be the same as some other experience from the past. Then another unconscious assumption is made that the same outcome will be the result. Being in the present prevents this because being in the present involves accepting things *as they are*.

The second essential part of awareness is being *non-judgmental and non-defensive* about your sensory input and your feelings. Being judgmental means that you have thoughts or opinions which have emotional attachments to an experience or outcome. The outcome will be emotionally biased and is not about the experience itself. Judgements are based on past experiences and projected *possible* future outcomes. They are not based on the present. Being non-judgmental means that the present sensory input is analyzed free from emotional attachments to the past or anxieties for the future. An example is the statement, "Since I have been unhappily married in the past, another marriage will also be unhappy."

When you are judgmental, you are defensive. The fight-or-flight response is not only physically defensive but ego defensive as well. Whenever your emotions are attached to objects, experiences, situations, beliefs, and so forth, the ego is involved. The ego is the emotional identification that you make with that thing. Since you have identified with the object, etc., you and the object are one and the same: the actor and the action are same. It is the ego which then makes the judgment.

The third essential aspect of awareness is your *self-talk*. Your self-talk is crucial to creating self-rapport. Self-talk directs your unconscious mind and eventually your behavior. Along with visual imagery, self-talk is used to program your brain. You will also notice that your self-talk can help to direct the images that you are having as well.

Self-talk is both negative and positive. Negative self-talk can help to momentarily alleviate some emotional pain. Much negative self-talk is rationalization that is used to try to put things into perspective: "I am so *incompetent*. I can't do *anything* right," "I will *never* get the love I want. I have got *nothing* to offer *anyone*," "It is *his* fault I didn't get the promotion. It's not what you know; it's who," "Why does this *always* happen to me? I work hard and I *never* get anywhere." You will notice that these rationalizations, complaints and blaming actually *reinforce* the uncomfortable feelings as well as the problem and give the individual a good excuse to feel miserable.

Positive self-talk does just the opposite. It reinforces the pleasurable feelings that accompany the experience. Positive self-talk is more than just telling yourself something nice about yourself. It is redirecting and motivating your behavior and emotions. For example, if you had an experience that was emotionally trying, instead of chastising yourself (negative self-talk) you could say something like, "I really learned some important things from this upsetting experience and this is going to help me in so many ways from now on."[1] If a relationship had broken up or you were not able to make a connection with a desired person you can say, "I *prefer* to have this (person/relationship), but since it does not seem to be happening, there are a *lot* of other people in this world who are possible for a relationship." After you have made your positive statements follow them by direct action (e.g. in the case of a broken relationship, place yourself into a position to meet new people) and you will proceed with a good attitude.

The final part of acceptance is *the willingness to take responsibility for your thoughts, feelings and actions.* After accepting the sensory input for what it is without judgement and after accepting your feelings for what they are without blame, resentment, or judgement you are more in the here-and-now.

In self-rapport you need to match your internal feelings and internal dialogue with your external behavior. It is necessary to get deeply into your internal experiences What you are doing is identifying the experience. Then you are defining it through its different qualities. You are accepting it and its construction and integrating it into your present knowledge and learning repertoire by *congruently matching* your present internal experience with your present external experience.

Before the behavior is expressed there needs to be an awareness of the construction of the input. In the process of self-rapport this awareness is of both the internal processing and external input. One thing you must realize is that *literally all* of your experience is *internal*. As the theoretical physicists state: "Nothing exists outside of the mind. All that we perceive are external representations of internal concepts." Consequently, you are constantly matching your external world to your internal experience whether you realize it or not. Whether you have self-rapport or not, what you see (inside) is what you get (outside experience). So, your behavior matches your unconscious motivators and drivers. With self-rapport you are matching internals and externals more *congruently*. Further, with self-rapport you are able to make congruent changes without problems, frustrations, or unnecessary instability.

1. If you can't state the learning experience in positive terms you really haven't learned anything from the experience.

The last portion of the paradigm for achieving self-rapport is behavior. For self-rapport there has to be a congruency between what is going on inside and what is happening on the outside. You have already gone through the sensory input, the analysis of that input, the processing of the input and its analysis, the associations with the past experiences and the present situation. Now you are keeping in the present and not judging in any way or analyzing what is going on inside. Here you will be coming to conclusions based on the here-and-now. Finally, you reach the point of decision-making regarding the output of the experience. This is where you generate the appropriate behavior which is congruent to the input and what is happening internally. It is here where you generate the appropriate behavior based on awareness, acceptance and non-judgement. The steps that you can take to achieve self-rapport in any situation can be summarized as:

1. Relax, take a deep breath and begin to become aware of your feelings. Verbalizing your feelings helps you to identify and define them. Once this is done it is easier to accept them. Verbalizing your feelings also disassociates you from them so they can be dealt with easier.

2. Identify the subjective qualities of those feelings:
   a. location on or in the body and where
   b. shape
   c. size
   d. sharp or dull
   e. hot, cold, or warm
   f. hard or soft
   g. still or moving
   h. check also your internal visual and auditory processing.

3. Remain focused on your feelings staying with them and avoid intellectualizing them. Focus your consciousness on the totality of the *experience*. Let yourself accept your feelings for whatever they are. Allow your feelings to reach their natural outcome.

4. After you have allowed your feelings to be fully processed, accepted, and transformed, it is time to make a decision based upon the present input. You are now able to make decisions that are free from defensive emotions and judgements. You are on the path with more clarity and self-rapport.

5. Create a menu of choices and possibilities about the situation that created the lack of rapport in the first place. One technique that you can do is to get a sheet of paper and simply write down *every* possible solution you can think of no matter how unrealistic it may seem.

6. It is essential to recognize and accept those things that you have no power to change (i.e. other people and natural catastrophes).

7. Run the solutions through in your mind in order to determine which of the solutions would be the most desirable and will work best ecologically for yourself and your environment.

8. Make a decision. Act on that decision and follow through. As Richard Bandler, co-founder of Neuro-Linguistic Programming, has said, "If I do something and I do not succeed, I am miles ahead of where I would have been if I had done nothing at all."

9. Take the most appropriate solutions into the future and see the outcomes that they bring. Then work with the best of those solutions.

In order to achieve self-rapport you must discipline yourself through the practice of the exercises (or ones similar to these) discussed. No skill is useful if it is not practiced and self-rapport is a skill worth having. If you have the discipline and the awareness self-rapport offers, you will be empowered to create more rapport, harmony and balance within yourself. You will be able to develop and synergize balance and harmony in your world.

Here is a checklist that you can use to insure that you are in rapport with yourself prior to doing an aligning:

I.   Check your own state
   A.   Most important: *Be in the Present*
      1.   Notice what is going on in the here-and-now
      2.   Take your mind off of outside influences
      3.   Be aware of yourself and the environment
      4.   Check your own feelings
         a.   Be in a neutral state
         b.   Have no thoughts or distracted concentration
      5.   Stay focused
         a.   Train the mind to stay disciplined

B. Be Context Prepared
    1. Focus 100 percent on the context
        a. Both conscious and unconscious focus
        b. Expand your energy field to include the client
        c. Your focus is in the here-and-now as a One-ness
    2. Become aware of yourself, the environment, and the client
        a. Notice any lack of rapport

Once you have gained rapport with yourself you are able to focus on your client. Building and maintaining rapport is essential to meaningful communications. This establishes a common bond through which the client-therapist relationship can prosper. Paying close attention to both the verbal and non-verbal cues that your client is expressing is the first step in gaining rapport with your client.

The structure of client-centered rapport is based on *matching*. Matching is the process whereby you will adjust certain aspects of your external behavior to *approximate* in form and appearance those same characteristics of the client's external behavior. As an example, if your client tilts his/her head to the left you will do the same but to a lesser degree or angle.

The ongoing process of matching is referred to as *pacing*. Pacing is defined as: *A method of communication that quickly establishes rapport by matching or mirroring certain aspects of another's behavior.* What this means is that you will move in a corresponding fashion in response to shifts in the client's external behavior in an *ongoing* manner. You are essentially matching their *sequence* of movements, not a singular movement.

Pacing is reflecting back what another is already doing. In order to find out if your pacing is effective and rapport is being established, the next step is to *lead*. Leading is *adding new ideas into the ongoing feed-back loop.* This creates a new direction and can align resources in order to achieve goals. That is, all of the information is restructured around the course and direction.

The simplest formula for rapport is:

$$Observe \longrightarrow Calibrate \longrightarrow Match \longrightarrow Behavior = Rapport$$

In order to do the best work with your client it is necessary to have rapport with your unconscious. In order to have that check through this list:

1. Clear yourself with your client so as to not be part of the problem.

Make sure that you are in rapport with yourself before you begin to work with your client. It is so easy to project some aspect of yourself on to your client. It is done daily by many reputable therapists/counselors without them even knowing that they are doing it. In order to have the best effect on your client it is necessary to have what Carl Rogers called "unconditional positive regard." This is *total* acceptance of the client and what (s)he may say without any sort of judgement or preconceived ideas. It means setting aside your biases, misconceptions, personal experiences, values, beliefs, and so on and allowing the process to guide you. Researchers in hypnosis have found that a hypnotherapist's visual images may be projected on to the client in a hypnotherapy session. The rapport encountered in a *Psychokinesiology* (Pk) session tends to be much deeper than in hypnosis. Consequently, it is extremely important to make sure that your mind is open and clear for the process.

2. The subject *must* be willing to change.

You most likely heard it said that you cannot be of help to a client until that client actually wants the help. The same goes for a *Psychokinesiology* session. One of the questions that you can check for is this: "Yes or No, I want to make this change." The client could be stating consciously that (s)he wants the change but the unconscious may want to hold on to the behavior a little longer. That can be checked for as well. Only when the client is willing to change should you proceed.

3. Be in a neutral state.

The state of self-rapport is a neutral state. The total acceptance of unconditional positive regard is a neutral state. Allowing *yourself* to enjoy the experience of Pk is a neutral state. Being in a neutral state means that you have no perceived thoughts or even have any labels that you can attach to the client's behavior. To analyze his/her behavior takes you out of the realm of helping the client to judging him/her. The important thing is to be open and receptive focusing *only* on what you are doing because things will be happening quite quickly and you must be ready to deal with them as soon as they come up.

4. Tune in on yourself.

The first thing necessary for tuning in on yourself is to quiet the chatter that tends to go on in your mind and pay close attention to your own feelings. The excessive chatter tends to cause you to move into analysis and away from rapport. Not attending to your own feelings can cause a confusion with what is being experienced. It is easy to mistake your own feelings for those of another. When you do this you will be attempting to tell your client what (s)he is experiencing. The more you trust yourself and your abilities and skills the more you will be able to be of assistance to your client and the greater the change that will occur. As you tune in on yourself you will find that you will become more at-one with your client.

As you tune in more deeply with your client it is necessary to be open and receptive both emotionally and intuitively. This will help you to ask the most appropriate questions that will elicit the best responses from your client. This in turn will bring about the most powerful experience of change.

5. Pay attention to the levels of experience that *you* will be encountering throughout the Pk experience. Before you begin the Pk process and while you are gathering information and gaining rapport, make sure that you pay close attention to your client. Take everything into consideration about your client. Compare everything about that person. Look at what (s)he says the problem is. Find out what your client says (s)he wants. Pay attention to what is being said and how (s)he is acting. Stay focused with what is happening in the present. Where is your client in reference to the problem situation? Is (s)he in the past with it or projecting it into the future without realizing it? Make sure that *you* are *clear* on the problem as well. This is important because you need to look at *all* of the possible representations of the problem (i.e. from yourself, others you have known with a similar problem, even anyone the client has known with a similar problem). This will give you a broader spectrum from which to work and more possible outcomes that are available to your client.

6. See to it that you are in a receptive state. Begin by checking your internal state. What are you feeling? What are your thoughts? Do you have any preconceived ideas regarding your client or the stated problem? Then make sure that yours and your client's experience are one and the same. This is where your rapport building skills will come into play. If you feel any trepidation before you start you are going to have to take the time to remove yourself from the experience. One sure way of making sure that you are in a receptive state is to be in a state of wonder concerning your client and what you will learn more about the Pk process, the problem and yourself during the experience.

CHAPTER 6

QUESTIONING

After gaining rapport with your client the next step is to find out what the problem appears to be. That is, what is it that your client wants to change? Remember that whenever your client is going toward something, he is going away from something else. Remember, even though he is saying that he does not want one thing, he is continuing to go toward it. So, when your client tells you what he thinks the problem may be he is also giving you an indication of what he wants. What you need to do is *not* tell him what *you* think he wants but to get him to indicate it himself. In this way his unconscious automatically begins to attach to the resources necessary for the change.

The questions that you ask direct your client how to think. Every question sets a direction. They direct and induce your client to reorganize the information in such a way that the answer can be accessed. The quality of the question directs the quality of the information you receive. Make sure that you ask questions with purpose and purposefully. The intent is to get at your client's data base. One thing to remember is to *stay with the original idea or question until you get the answer*. There will be times when your client will be going off into realms that may appear to have something to do with your basic intent but in reality have little to do with anything except keeping away from the actual response. It is alright to say, "What I asked was _____." You may have to reword your original question in order bypass any defensive posturing. Going off track is often a defensive move. So, with a little bit of insistence you will get a reply that will be approaching the appropriate response. The main idea for the questioning is to clear up the thinking of your client so that you can get to the actual problem. With that clarity comes direction.

Begin your questioning to find out what the problem is by simply asking your client what he would like to work on. This is an innocuous question that has few emotional attachments and consequently has less of a chance of confronting any of the defenses. Most often with this question you will get one of two types of responses. The first response may be stating what it is that he *does not* want. This will get you nowhere because you need to know what your client actually wants. In goal setting, knowing what it is that you want is the first step to getting it. This is also the first step in directing the unconscious mind of your client to begin to look for resources that will help him to overcome the problem.

At this point the line of questioning could go something like this:

T - What is it that you'd like to work on today?

C - Well, I don't want to do X.

T - What is it that you *do* want to do?

C - What do you mean?

T - Whenever we go toward something we are going away from something else. You don't want to do X. What would you rather be doing instead?

C - Do you mean that if I am not <u>Xing</u>, what other thing could I be doing?

T - Exactly.

C - What I would like to do instead of doing X is to do Y.

The second type of response you may get is to mention something that is thought to be the problem. This is most often not the problem. The questioning can go like this:

T - What is it that you want to work on today?

C - I don't seem to be able to motivate myself to do anything.

T - Do you mean that whenever there is something that you have to get done you don't want to do it?

C - It is not that I don't want to do it. I just don't seem to have the energy to do it.

T - So, do you think that you want to work on getting more motivation? That will help you get those things done?

C - Yes. I want to have more motivation.

T - If you did have more motivation what would you do? (You could also continue your line of questioning with: "Let me ask you again, be specific, if you were more motivated, *what* would you do?" From here you could then generate questions to find out if the client was lacking motivation or was actually procrastinating.)

C - Then I could get to those things that I have to do but have not been able to.

T - So, a lack of motivation keeps you from getting to things that you say you want to do?

C - Yes. Something seems to be stopping me from getting things done.

T - Something seems to be stopping you. What is stopping you?

C - Every time that I start to do one of them the other ones are in the back of my mind and I get overwhelmed.

T - But why do you keep putting off doing those things?

C - What do you mean?

T - You keep putting things off. That isn't a lack of motivation. Is it?

C - No, I guess it isn't.

T - It seems to me the problem isn't motivation but procrastination. You keep putting things off and by the time you get around to doing them there's more than you feel you can handle and you become overwhelmed. So you keep on procrastinating. Wouldn't it be easier to get things done when they need to be done instead of putting them off?

C - Yes.

T - Does procrastination seem more like what may be keeping you from getting things done?

C - Yes. That makes more sense.

If you begin your *Psychokinesiology* session based on the direct statement of the client this can lead into a circuitous testing process where little will be accomplished and the actual problem will be circumvented with testing rhetoric that makes little if any sense to either you or your client. The most difficult part of this is that the problem will still be hidden under layers of unconnected experiences and emotions (i.e. defenses). It will be a slow process to get to the actual *Time of Origin* of the problem. So, the above procedure could go something like this:

T - What do you want to work on today?

C - I don't seem to be able to motivate myself to do anything.

T - Do you mean that whenever there is something that you have to get done you don't want to do it?

C - It is not that I don't want to do it. I just don't seem to have the energy to do it.

T - So, you want to work on becoming more motivated? And you feel that being more motivated will be the thing that will get all those things done?

C - Yes. I want to be more motivated.

T - If you were more motivated what would you do?

C - Then I could do a lot more things.

T - So, by having more motivation you get more things done?

C - Yes. If I was more motivated I would be doing more things.

T - How can having more motivation help you get more things done?

C - I would get busy on those things I haven't been able to get to.

T - What stops you from doing those things now?

C - I am not motivated enough.

T - So, by being more motivated then you can get those other things done?

C - Yes.

As you can see from this rather general questioning procedure, you end up going around and around the same thing with no resolution. You can easily mistake the circuitous rhetoric for the problematic behavior that needs changed. This is not the problem. You can tell it is not the appropriate response because it is very not specific and your client keeps saying the same thing over and over and the questioning process comes to no true resolution. This will get you into a bind and when you begin the Pk process you could become more confused because the chances are you will be getting some conflicting readings and it will take a lot longer time to induce any changes. There is also the chance that the *Time of Awareness* of the problem will be mistaken for the *Time of Origin* and you will find yourself having to go over the same things several times.

An important thing to remember is that the Pk process is for and about *your client*. If your client begins to talk about what someone else is doing or how someone else is acting, bring him back to the time and place where you are. If you get something like:

T - So, why do you keep putting off doing the things you have to do?

C - I am just not happy where I work. Bob is always there looking like he is waiting until I make a mistake.

T - What does this have to do with what we're talking about? What does Bob have to do with you putting off doing the things that you have to do?

C - Bob should act better toward me. He is the one who needs the help.

T - We're here now for you to make changes. When Bob decides that he needs to make some changes in his life, give him my phone number and we'll make the changes he wants. Now, why do you keep putting off the things that you have to do?

As you can see, this line of questioning brings you back to the main point. Often, when the client goes off in a different direction it is very subtle and can be hardly noticeable. When this happens it is very easy to become side-tracked.

T - So, why do you keep putting off those things that you have to do?

C - It is not that I keep putting them off, some of them are more important than others.

T - Then, you have prioritized what is important and what is not?

C - Yes. I guess you could say that. The ones that are more important are at the top of the list.

T - So, the ones at the top of the list you work on first.

C - Yes. I do what I can to get them done.

T - Do you get the jobs at the top of the list done all of the time?

C - Most of the time.

T - What do you do about the ones that you don't get done?

C - They get done eventually.

T - But they do get done?

C - Eventually.

T - Then, the problem you want to work on is a lack of motivation so you can get all of your jobs done.

C - Yes, I guess that's it.

From the direction of the questioning here you got so far removed from the main point that there was no way that anything can be useful for your further consideration. So the importance of pertinent questioning right at the beginning cannot be overstated.

Questioning is an art. In order for it to be most effective it must be done in such a way that you know exactly what information that you want to elicit. In order to do that you must know how to formulate your questions.

In order to be able to ask pertinent questions it is necessary to understand the types of information that questions can bring. We will begin with the basic questions.

The *who* question uncovers the specific person involved in the response:
Who specifically doesn't listen to you?

The *what* question goes for specific information such as the reason or purpose, the worth of something, or information not fully understood.
What was on your mind when you made that comment?
What is so important about John's opinion?
What did you mean when you said, "I don't think that whatever I do in this instance will bring about a resolution?"

The *when* question looks for a specific time or circumstance.
When did you decide that?
When are you going to make that change?

A *where* question finds the specific place, circumstance, or position.
Where is your desk in the office?
Where are you in the office hierarchy?
Where do you stand on that issue?

When you ask *why* you are seeking the reason, cause, or purpose.
Why did you write that note to her?
Why does someone choose the mate that they do?
Why did you return to your original opinion after you found out it wasn't useful?

The why question is usually not a really good question to ask in a therapeutic situation. To find the reason or cause of something simply ask, "**What reason do you have** for doing that?" It is a more specific question.

It is the *how* question that finds out in what manner, the extent or degree, the state or condition, the reason behind something, the effect and the meaning.

How did the "cold war" begin?
How was your thinking different after everyone's job was outlined clearly?
How did she fare after her desk was moved?
How did you come to that conclusion?
How are we to understand your reasoning?

There are certain thinking and language patterns that you can use to help you to formulate your questions. If you follow these procedures you will be able to find the most valuable information. Some of the examples below will be in general. Let us begin with the type of thinking that is being used. There will be an example of the language of that type of thinking. Next, there will be examples of questions that can be asked. Finally, you will see what information will be retrieved by the questioning.

All-or-Nothing Thinking

With this type of thinking *everything* must be included in the category. If you are not able to succeed at something then *everything* has failed.

C - *If I don't act **perfectly** correct at that time then I'll be a **total** moron.*
T_1- *Will you be a **total** moron?*
T_2- *Is a **perfect** action the only worthwhile action? Does an action **have to be perfect** in order to be correct?*

The information retrieved: Specific classifications.

Universal Thinking

The words to listen for with this category are: *always, never, ever, every, nothing, none, everybody, everyone, anyone, just, only, everything, any, can't,* and *no one*. The language pattern shows an exaggeration which is totally out of proportion to the situation.

C_1 - *I **always** screw up when I try. **Nothing ever** goes right for me.*
T_1 - ***Always? Nothing? Ever?***
T_2 - *Are there times when things **do** go right for you?*
T_3 - ***Never** under **any** circumstances does **anything ever** go right for you?*
C_2 - *She refused me. I'll **never** have another date again.*
T_4 - *Does her refusal mean you'll **never** have a date with **anyone ever again**?*
C_3 - *He didn't thank me. I'm not appreciated by **anyone**.*
T_5 - *Does his not thanking you mean that **no one** appreciates you?*

The information retrieved: The specifics and effects.

Mind-Reading

This sort of thinking assumes that you have the ability to get into another's thoughts and thinking processes. This is used quite a bit in our daily lives when dealing with others.

C_1 - *He doesn't care about me.*

T_1 - *How do you know that?*

C_2 - *He does that because he **hates** me.*

T_2 - *What evidence do you have that he **hates** you?*

T_3 - *Could there be other possible explanations for his actions?*

The information retrieved: The evidence or proof of the evaluation.

Prophetic Thinking

Prophetic thinking is predicting the future before you have even begun doing something. In essence, you are saying it is going to turn out badly no matter what you do.

C_1 - *If I try that I **know** it won't work.*

T_1 - *Do you **know** for **certain** that it won't work?*

C_2 - *John didn't do it. What makes you think I can do it?*

T_2 - *Just because someone else didn't do it, who says that you can't do it?*

C_3 - *Even if I try I am **positive** that I'll fail.*

T_3 - *Even if you did it before and it didn't work, how do you know that it won't work now?*

T_4 - *In what ways are you positive?*

T_5 - *How **positive** are you that you'll fail?*

The information retrieved: The evidence and experience leading to the evaluation.

Down-playing

When you down-play something you are discounting the desirable qualities or achievements until they are almost non-existent.

C - *Anyone could have done it. I wasn't that important in what happened. In fact, I didn't even need to be there.*

T_1 - *How do you know that **anyone** could have done it?*

T_2 - *Anyone? According to who could **anyone** have been able to do it?*

T_3 - *Who specifically could have done it?*

The information retrieved: Specific references.

Cause/Effect

Cause/effect is a form of emotional reasoning. It makes an emotional and illogical connection between one thing and another. The fact is, both the subject and the object are different.

C_1 - *She yelled at me. She **hates** me.*

T_1 - *Does her yelling at you **really** mean she **hates** you?*

T_2 - *Could there be another reason for her yelling at you?*

T_3 - *Does yelling **always** mean **hate**?*

C_2 - *When he looks at me that way he **makes** me so angry.*

T_4 - *How does his looking that way **make** you so angry?*

T_5 - *What would happen if you didn't get angry?*

T_6 - *Can you think of a time when someone looked at you the same way and you didn't get angry?*

Information retrieved: The illogical reasoning.

Parental Injunctions

These are personal demands, demands that you place on to others and the world. These are seen in the words; *should, would, have to, need to,* and *must.* These all result in feelings of shame and guilt.

C_1 - *I **have** to do it that way.*

T_1 - *What would happen if you broke that rule?*

T_2 - *Are you 100% **sure** of the consequences being so bad if you did it differently?*

T_3 - *Who said that you **have to** do it that way?*

C_2 - *He **should** do it this way.*

T_4 - *What makes you think he **should**?*

T_5 - *According to who **should** he do it that way?*

T_6 - *Where is written in stone that he **should** do it that way?*

Information retrieved: Specific source or consequences.

Mislabeling

When a behavior is labeled it limits the person's ability to go beyond that label. The label is an emotional tag which is based on one or a limited number of experiences in which the person deletes any information to the contrary.

C_1 - *I couldn't get that job. I am a **loser**.*

T_1 - *Does **not** getting **that** job **make** you a **loser**?*

T_2 - *How are you a **loser** just because you didn't get **that** job?*

T_3 - *Does **not** getting that job mean that you **can't** get one just as good or **better**?*
Information retrieved: Specific reasons.

Personal Blaming

In this process the person blames himself for what went on even though he did not have any control over it. This usually involves a decision made by another person.

C_1 - *She canceled our date. I'm such a **failure** that I can't get someone to keep a date with me.*

T_1 - *What other possible reasons could there be for her canceling the date?*

T_2 - *Just because she canceled this date what makes you think she'll **never** go out with you again?*

T_3 - *What **makes** you a **failure** because she canceled the date?*

T_4 - *Does canceling a date mean **failure**?*
Information retrieved: Other possible reasons.

Over-Exaggeration

The person using this pattern sees everything that has the slightest tinge of negativity as a catastrophe. Things that are not that important in life are given an extreme amount of significance.

C_1 - *He has **all** of the luck. I'll **never** get to have anyone like that.*

T_1 - *What evidence do you have that **he** has **all** of the luck?*

T_2 - *Does his getting that person mean there is none other like that person in the whole world?*

T_3 - *How bad is this really?*

T_4 - *How likely is it that you will **never** have anyone like that?*

T_5 - *What is the **worst** that could happen if you **never** did have someone like that?*

T_6 - *Does his having that person mean he has **all** of the luck?*
Information retrieved: Evidence for evaluation.

Impossibility

Impossibility is noted with the words; *can't couldn't, unable,* and *impossible.* These limit the person's ability to make choices and to become personally directed and motivated.

C_1 - *I can't do it no matter how hard I try.*
T_1 - *What stops you?*
T_2 - *What would(n't) happen if you did(n't)?*

This line of questioning varies through: What would happen if you did?; What wouldn't happen if you did?, and so on.

T_3 - *How sure are you that you can't do it?*
T_4 - *What makes you so sure of that?*
T_5 - *What if you can do it?*
T_6 - *What's the worst that can happen if you couldn't do it?*

This line of questioning varies through: What's the worst that can happen if you could?; What's the best thing that could happen if you couldn't?, and so on.

Information retrieved: Identifies subjective causes and effects.

The beginning questioning procedure can turn out to be rather complicated. There are times when you will be literally going in circles with a particular question. It is important to look for the fear, anxiety, helplessness, and guilt which underlies most problems. If you do not seem to be finding the fear or anxiety and etc. you will most likely end up going around in circles. When this happens you will know that you are most likely dealing with a defense. Then you will need to change your line of questioning coming at it from a different perspective. Eventually, you will come to a point when you say something that triggers an "ah-ha!" type of response in your client. As soon as this happens you will find an almost immediate change in your client that will automatically begin an internal reorganization. Then, as soon as you begin working with him you will find getting at the core of the problematic behavior quick and easy. In essence, when your beginning questioning is appropriately constructed you prepare your client's mind so that it can make its own changes. Bringing the actual problematic behavior into conscious awareness allows the unconscious mind to readjust the resources your client has available.

The following is an annotated transcription of the basic questioning procedure to get at a problem behavior.

T - *What is the problem that you would like to work on today?*
C - *I have a bad habit that I want to get rid of.*
    This response is not to the point. It is vague and general. This indicates that the client, on the unconscious level, was most likely in a defensive posture attempting to not directly deal with the problem.

T - *What is it?*
C - *Well..., every time I get nervous I overeat.*
    The "well" response was drawn out. Another indicator that the client did not want to get to the point.

T - *When was the last time that you did that?*
C - *Yesterday.*
    Much of the time a client will respond with more than a one-word response. Many times you will get more information than you really want and have to wade through a description that can easily get you off the point. A single word response indicates that the client feels uncomfortable (guilt) when thinking about or discussing the problem.

T - *How about the time before that?*
C - *A couple of days ago.*
    Again, there is reluctance, and probably even embarrassment, when dealing with the problem.

T - *So, if you don't get nervous you wouldn't overeat?*
    What the counselor is doing here is trying to find out if it is nervousness which causes the overeating or if it is something else.

C - *Yes, if I didn't get nervous I wouldn't overeat?*
    It is not until a client has gone through a few months of traditional therapy or counseling that he will have a pretty good idea of what may be the cause of the problem. This response of the client is more for the counselor than the client. It was not a definite statement and the tone of voice of the client was ambivalent.

T - *Then, you would like to stop getting nervous?*
This question is a huge generalization. It is impossible to not get nervous in life. To respond as the client did indicates he does not realize that nervousness is not the problem and that nervous does not automatically mean overeat.

C - *Yes.*
The client's voice was not concise and direct, so the problem is not what the client thinks it is.

T - *Does not getting nervous mean that you'll stop overeating?*
This question puts together what the client has claimed was the problem. Once the client hears the problem put together in such a way he usually begins an unconscious shift where there is a realization that the two concepts do not fit.

C - *Yes, I think so.*
This comment indicates that a shift is taking place and the client realizes on the unconscious level that nervous does not mean overeat.

T - *Can you think of a time when you were nervous and **did not** overeat?*
With this question the counselor is showing the client that what he said is not what actually is. What the counselor is doing is showing the client that nervousness is not the problem.

C - *Let me think. Yes, a few days ago.*
The client has to search through his experiences and come up with at least one response that shows that nervousness does not equal overeating. Once this is done then he will have to find another reason for his overeating.

T - *So, getting nervous doesn't necessarily mean that you'll overeat.*
The proof of the fallacy of the statement must be shown to the client. In this way the client can see that there are other possibilities.

C - *No, I guess it doesn't. I guess that I just want to stop overeating then.*
This is a standard response. If nervousness is not the problem then overeating must be the problem. Overeating is the *symptom*. Something

else is the cause. If you attempt to do a *Resource Realigning[1]* with this information you will constantly be brought back because something else needs to be done.

T - *Let's do one thing at a time. Getting nervous doesn't mean overeating, right?*
It is very easy to get off of the track here. It is necessary to remember what it is that you are doing. Here the counselor knows that overeating is not the problem and the client is brought back by showing this to him.

C - *Right.*
This is nothing more than the elicitation of the direction. It is bringing the client's internal processes back to the present.

T - *If getting nervous doesn't mean that you'll overeat then something else must be what causes you to overeat.*
Here the counselor seeks to get more agreement and congruency with the idea that overeating is a symptom of something other than nervousness.

C - *Yes. I guess that's true.*
The client has been brought back to the present and agreement has been made that brings a deeper internal search.

T - *Is there something that you can think of that all of the overeating sessions have in common?*
This is a very good question to ask. It is similar to the question previously asked; "Can you think of a time when you overate and were not nervous?"

---

[1] *Resource Realigning* has also been referred to as a "clearing" by many kinesiologists. What *Resource Realigning* does is readjust unconscious internal states so that they are congruent to the accomplishing of a particular goal thus allowing the possibility for more choices and access to more of your potential.

C - *Overeating.*

When the client expresses humor it indicates one of two things: 1) he is more relaxed and more willing to talk, or 2) the client is a bit nervous and is attempting to hide something. In this case the first indicator appears to be more appropriate.

T - *Well, that goes without saying. Can you think of a commonality?*

The counselor is directing the client to go deeper and into the past to relate each of the experiences of overeating together.

C - *Let me see. Hm-m-m. Well, there is the nervousness.*

The client is back to nervousness again. If this happens this can indicate that the client is defending the real reason or what the client has called "nervous" is mislabeled.

T - *What kind of nervousness is it?*

The counselor is asking for the client to define the term "nervous" to make sure the client understands what he is experiencing.

C - *It is like I get a little scared and wonder what's going to happen.*

Once the client has put into words his feelings then it is easier to deal with the emotions. What you will notice is that the client has mislabeled the emotion and this mislabeling process is a protective device.

T - *You feel a little scared and begin thinking about what's **going** to happen? That doesn't sound like nervousness to me. It sounds like anxiety. When you're anxious you're going to get a little scared and worry about the future. So, what you're actually saying is that whenever you get anxious you overeat. Does that sound correct?*

Here the counselor shows the client that he has mislabeled an emotion and has reframed it giving it a more appropriate label; one that fits the problem and one in which a *Resource Realigning* will be quick, easy, and direct.

C - *Yes, that is it. Right before I begin overeating I feel anxious.*

This is a point of realization for the client. For the longest time it was thought that nervousness led to overeating. Now, with this new revelation, it has been found that anxiety leads to overeating.

T - *What are you anxious about? What do you say to yourself?*
It is not wise to begin doing a *Resource Realigning* at this point. You will need to know what your client is anxious about as well as what kind of anxiety you are dealing with.

C - *It could be a lot of things but mostly I say things like: "What if I do this and somebody doesn't like me?" or "What if I do that and it doesn't work out?" or "What if I say something and everyone laughs?"*
This is a more focused response. With it you can get the idea that the anxiety that you are dealing with has to do with relationships.

T - *So, whenever you get anxious about what other people are thinking about you then you overeat?*
You must realize that it is a *specific* type of anxiety that leads to the overeating. Simply asking: "So, whenever you get anxious you overeat?" is too general. Your client will respond with an affirmative response but when you do your *Resource Realigning* you may get some confusing responses. You may get even more specific to find out who these other people are. That is unnecessary because you may not need to find that out for the realigning session.

C - *Yes.*
That was a congruent response.

T - *You also mentioned that there were times that you could think of when you weren't nervous and still overate.*
This is a looping device. What it does is brings the client back to the beginning. When a loop is done the unconscious has to re-associate with everything that was said from the point of the loop back to the present.

C - *Yes.*

T - *Were you anxious then?*
This question sends the client into an internal search to find the validity of the anxiety/overeat pattern over that of nervousness/overeat.

C - *Let me think. Yes. I can recall one time when I thought, "What if I don't lose weight, then nobody will ever want me."*

Once the client has found the first example others will follow closely behind.

T - *Then could we say feeling anxious means that you will overeat?*

This reframes the pattern to one that is more congruent internally.

C - *Yes. Whenever I feel anxious. Yes.*

Congruency is agreement on all levels. The tone of voice and body language were totally congruent with this statement.

T - *Anxiety is a fear. It is a fear of the future; of something that **might** happen. What is it that you are afraid might or might not happen?*

By understanding what your client is anxious about can help you to focus the *Resource Realigning* with proper questioning during the realigning process. This will help your client to decide what he actually wants instead of what he does not want.

C - *I am afraid that I might not be able to be successful in a relationship.*

The chances are this statement is a generalization referring itself to many more aspects of the client's life than relationships alone. You may need to explore this later in another session. It is also highly possible that once the realigning is done the generalization into other aspects of the client's life will also dissolve.

T - *Then, you are afraid of succeeding in relationships? That is the same thing that you said earlier when you stated that no one would ever want you because you are overweight. So you overeat whenever thoughts of not succeeding begin to surface?*

The counselor went from a specific to a generalization because on the unconscious level an association will be made between success in relationships and general success. This increases the chances for the realigning process to clear any other success problems.

C - *Yes. That seems to be it. Wow!.*

This is a moment of enlightenment. There is a congruent response on both the conscious and unconscious levels.

T - *What if you are able to have a successful relationship, would you stop overeating?*

This question brings around to the client a concept that was not considered previously. By posing it this brings in the possibility of doing two things at the same time.

C - *If I did succeed then I'd be worried about how long it would last.*

The client side-stepped answering the question. This indicates that he has not considered the possibility of having both.

T - *What if you are able to have a successful relationship, would you stop overeating?*

Restating the question creates an anxiety in the client. With this client the counselor wants to force the client to consider the possibility of having both.

C - *You mean that I can have both? I never considered having both.*

Once the client can see himself having both a successful relationship and stopping overeating, the possibilities are opened up.

T - *What is stopping you from succeeding at having both now?*

What the client needs to do is to look at the stuck state and find ways of overcoming that state and becoming successful.

C - *Well, I am overweight.*

This is a rationalization; a cop-out and has nothing to do with not succeeding in relationships or in success in general.

T - *What does being overweight have to do with not being successful in a relationship or not being successful at all? I'm sure that you have noticed many overweight people who are successful in relationships and in their everyday lives. So, how is it that you are the **only** person in the whole world who is overweight and **can't** be successful or have a successful relationship?*

What the counselor is doing here is taking the generalization out of the process and showing the client that his thinking is illogical. Weight has nothing to do with the situation.

C - *Well, that all makes sense. Being overweight is not the problem. Just like you said, it's a symptom and something else is the problem: the anxiety.*

Here is another revelation for the client. What is slowly happening is that the mind of the client is being readjusted. This readjustment procedure really helps the *Resource Realigning* to be more effective.

T - *That is absolutely correct! The bottom line is the generalized anxiety you have toward being successful. Tell me this, how do you feel about being successful?*

Again, there is a restating of the problem behavior. This final question is designed to find out if there are layers underlying the fear of success.

C - *I feel anxious when I think of being successful.*
T - *Well, what do you feel about loosing weight?*
C - *I feel anxious when I think about losing weight, too!*

You will notice that anxiety seems to be pretty much pervasive. Being afraid of succeeding is not uncommon. Succeeding at success and succeeding at losing weight have a common thread weaving through them with this client.

T - *That's interesting. Here you are afraid of succeeding at success and you're afraid of succeeding at losing weight because if you did then you might just succeed at life. Sounds to me like you have gotten yourself into a loop where if you lose weight you might succeed and in order to succeed you have to lose weight. What would it take for you to succeed at both?*

Another loop is created by forcing the client to reconsider succeeding at both success and at losing weight.

C - *I'm not sure what you mean.*
T - *What do you have to get rid of to be successful at stopping overeating and at reaching your goals?*

Now, specific plans are being drawn up on both the conscious and unconscious levels to achieve success in both areas.

C - *Hm-m-m. To quit being afraid of being successful.*

T - *That's a pretty general statement. If you were able to get rid of that fear of succeeding would you stop overeating and achieve your goals?*

C - *Yes! That makes a lot of sense!*

T - *Okay, let's start here with the fear of succeeding.*

We now have what the client is moving away from. Now we need to get what he wants to move toward.

C - *That sounds like a good place to start for me. Now things are beginning to make sense.*

T - *Good. What would you rather have instead of that fear?*

Now we begin to move directly in on what the client wants instead of what he does not want.

C - *I never thought of that before. Let's see. What would I rather have instead of that fear of success?*

T - *Right. What would you be doing if you didn't have that fear?*

This is a restating of the previous question. By doing this you are allowing the unconscious to do a wider range of searching for an appropriate response.

C - *I would be able to achieve my goals!*

T - *That's good. Now, what does that mean?*

C - *I would stick to my choices and not waver.*

Now we are coming to the root of the problem. It is most likely a lack of commitment that is causing him to be unsuccessful at losing weight, at relationships, and at becoming successful.

T - *You would stick to your choices and not waver? What does not sticking to your choices indicate?*

It is important that you get the client to state exactly what the problem is in a congruent manner. Once this has happened you will find it much easier to get the *Resource Realigning* done. It is also important that you use personal pronouns (i.e. you and yours). Never used the third person (e.g. one, a person, someone). The third person depersonalizes the question and gives the client an emotional out.

C - *It could mean that I haven't considered all of the options.*
This is a defensive statement. He is trying to keep from making a commitment as to the problem as well.

T - *Does that make sense to you in this instance?*
Again, this is getting the client to come away from any defensiveness and stating what the problem actually is.

C - *No. I think that for me it means that I don't stick to my commitments to myself.*
This is what you have been waiting for. You now have a direct statement of the problem.

T - *I wonder if you noticed that your first statement; "It could mean that someone has not considered all of the options" is not committing yourself to stating what the problem is?*
C - *I never realized that. I really haven't committed myself to achieving any kind of success.*
T - *Good.*
C - *I need to keep my commitments to myself. If I did that I would be much more successful.*
T - *Right! That is where we will begin.*
Now, you are ready to begin the *Psychokinesiology* session. As you can see, You must prepare your client's mind so that it is already opened up and is considering possibilities. Once the possibilities have been considered the unconscious enlists and aligns the appropriate resources in order to create change.

CHAPTER 7

BASIC PK TESTING

You have done your questioning and have found out where to begin. You have something to adjust which your client has congruently decided upon himself. The fact of the matter is that with the appropriate questioning your client's *unconscious* will bring out from itself where to begin. The appropriate questioning will also begin the process of change. You will then find that a *Resource Realigning* will be much easier and you will have a more in-depth response from your client.

Psychokinesiology makes use of muscle testing in order to gather information from your client's unconscious. It tests the strength or weakness of a thought or idea on behavior. Muscle testing is the key to unlocking the unconscious processes quickly and effectively. With it you can find out exactly what the unconscious is thinking and feeling about a thought, an idea, or a behavior. The theory behind the use of muscle testing is that the unconscious communicates *through* the body. By applying a *slight* pressure to a particular muscle you can establish that communication. Once that communication is established then you can get a lot of really valuable and useful information that can assist your client in her change.

Most people who use muscle testing are familiar with the arm extended outward to the side testing the deltoid muscle. **(Figure 7-1)**. This can be done standing up or sitting down. You can actually use any muscle or muscle group for testing. In order to create a circuit while doing testing and get more reliable readings while standing or sitting it is best to turn your head to the right and have your client turn her head

Figure 7-1   Testing the Deltoid Muscle

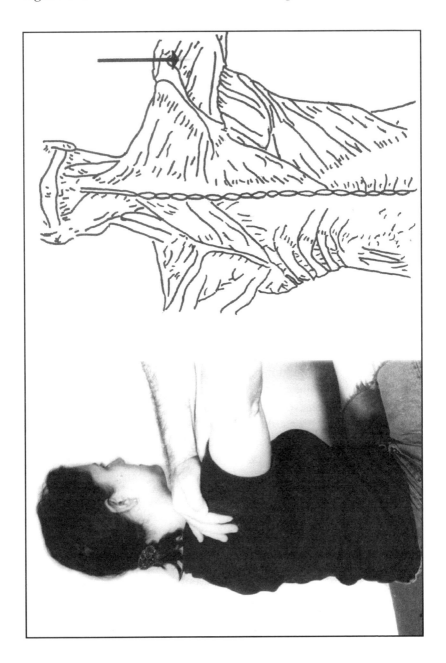

to the left. Also, if you are either standing or sitting while testing, do not look into your client's face. Make sure your client is not looking at you either. This will affect the reading that you will get. Your client will be reacting more to your face (e.g. a smile) and not to the question.

Many people who are new with muscle testing think that with a weak response the arm must drop fully. That is not true. A weak response is also indicated with a quick drop and a return to the strength position. **(Figure 7-2)** In essence, any change in the response can be considered a weak response. So, it is important that you *calibrate clearly* for yourself.

In *Psychokinesiology* you will test using mainly the arm(s) as well. The difference is that the client is lying down on her back. Lying down induces relaxation, lowers anxiety, and promotes regression. The advantage of this position is that it permits the expression of feelings that may otherwise produce an overpowering state of anxiety. You can be standing at your client's head and your client's arms will be extended and leaning back about at a 45° angle. **(Figure 7-3)** You may also be standing beside your client testing with one arm. **(Figure 7-4)** The testing will be done by having your client resist your push toward his feet. By standing behind your client testing both arms you will be able to see how each hemisphere of the brain will be reacting in the process. It is interesting when you make a statement while testing at your client's head. You can find one arm weak and the other strong. **(Figure 7-5)** This indicates that one hemisphere of the brain is strong with the idea and the other side is weak. The meaning of this is that the brain is not congruent with the idea or some aspect of the idea. This incongruency prevents your client from making changes in some aspect of his life. You will find the *Retrograde Polarities* important here. *Retrograde Polarities* will be discussed more shortly.

Let us begin with your client lying down on the table. The first thing that you will need to do is to calibrate to your client's muscle strength. Stand at the head of the table with your hands on your client's wrists and simply tell her, "When I say 'hold' I'm going to push against your arms and I want you to resist the push. Okay? Hold." With this you will gauge how much energy your client is exerting. You may have to do it several times. There is no other reason for this other than getting the timing between your stating "hold" and your client's resistance.

There are some other calibration tests that you may want to do as well. They can tell you if your client is "wired correctly." Your client

A Weak Response

Figure 7-2

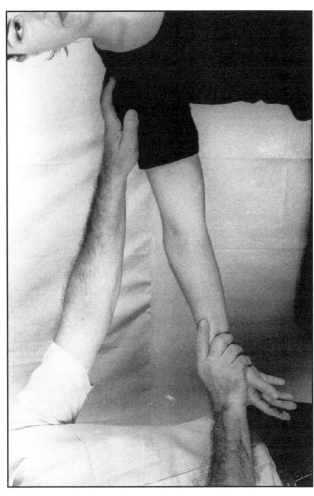

Two things are important to remember whenever doing muscle testing:

1) It is a good habit to support the arm being tested by placing a hand on your client's shoulder; and

2) A weak response isn't always indicated with a noticeable drop of the arm. There may be nothing more than an instant of weakness and the arm returning to the testing position.

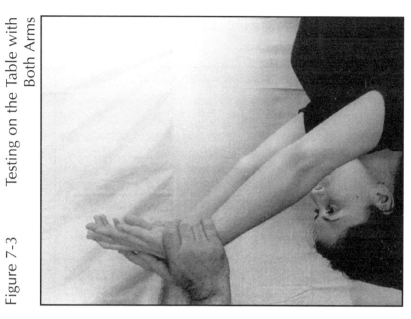

Figure 7-3   Testing on the Table with Both Arms

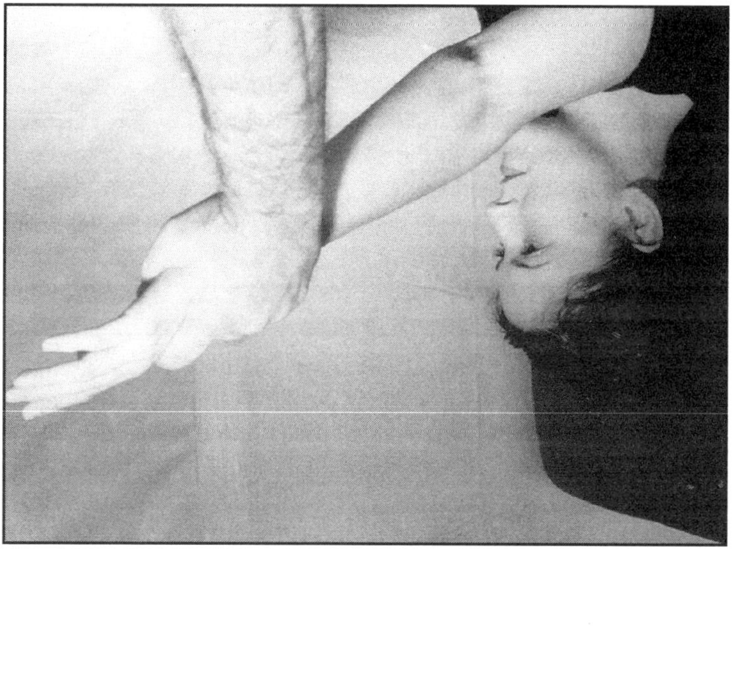

Figure 7-4   Testing on the Table with One Arm

Figure 7-5   Testing Both Arms

Often when testing both arms you will get a strong
response in one arm and a weak response in the other.
This indicates that one side of the brain has a feeling different from the other side of the brain in reference to the
idea of being tested.

needs to be responding appropriately; that there is no *Internal Reversal* and these tests will show that. The first test is that of the client's name. Have your client repeat after you, "My name is (<u>correct name</u>). Hold." and test. The test should be strong. Then have your client state after you, "My name is (<u>incorrect name</u>). Hold." and test. The test should be weak. If this test shows an *Internal Reversal* what you will need to do is one of several things: 1) touch your index and middle fingers between the eyebrows of your client and test. **(Figure 7-6)** The test should be weak. If not then you will need to correct it; or 2) have your client take her free hand and place it on the top of her head palm down and test. **(Figure 7-7)** It should be strong. Then have her place the same hand palm up on the top of her head and test. It should be weak. If the test is reversed you

Figure 7-6   First Internal Reversal Test

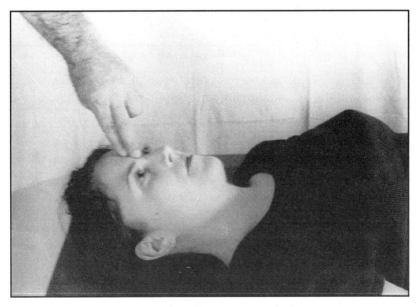

If you are getting responses that don't agree with the questions or statements then something is reversed in your client's thinking processes. For example, if you get a weak response on your client's name then you have a reversal. You need to then correct it. Sometimes you may get appropriate responses for a while then a reversal appears. Check it with the basic name and place checks.

Figure 7-7   Testing for an Internal Reversal

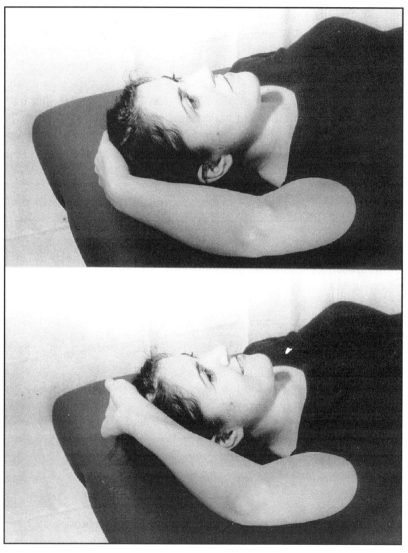

With the palm on the top of the head the test should be strong and weak when facing upward.

will need to correct the reversal. The simplest way to make this correction is by having your client drink a glass of distilled or fresh water then test again with the name test. **(Figure 7-8)** If this does not correct the reversal you can snap your fingers in front of her face and state; "Be here now!" and test. **(Figure 7-9)** If this does not work then tap the forehead several times and test. **(Figure 7-10)** These are simple tests and any one of them can work to correct an *Internal Reversal*. If none of these clear up the reversal then you will need to do a standard *Resource Realigning*. How to do this will be discussed in a later chapter. It is interesting to note that this reversal tends to occur much less with your client lying down than when sitting or standing up.

The next calibration is that of an internal rapport with your client's unconscious. This is easily done by stating; "Think of me. Hold!" and test. If this is weak it can indicate that there may be a lack of trust. The simplest way to correct this is to restate: "Think of trusting me *during* this process." This will most often get a strong response. If not you will have to proceed to doing a standard *Resource Realigning*.

There are several other optional calibration tests that you may want to do. For example, you may want to do the place test: "Repeat. I am in (actual place) now. Hold." and "I am in (false place) now. Hold." Or you may want to test for a simple "yes" and "no" response. This last test is usually unnecessary because in the vast majority of instances a "yes" response is a strong response and a "no" response is a weak response.

You have done your basic calibrating and testing of your client. Now you will want to begin dealing with the problem. You can demonstrate to your client that there is an incongruent internal responding by stating both the positive and negative of the problem. You will begin by stating: "Think about (problem state). Hold." and test. When you test, it should be strong. Then you can state: "Think about (problem state) and say; 'I want to change (problem state).' Hold!" The test should be strong. Then state: "Think about (problem state) and say, 'I want to keep (problem state).' Hold!" This test should likewise be strong. This is an indicator of an incongruent or conflicting thought process. In Pk we call this incongruency a *Retrograde Polarity*.[1] A *Retrograde Polarity* is seen as

---

[1] This is called *Cognitive Dissonance* in Social Psychology and a *Sequential Incongruity* in Neuro-Linguistic Programming.

Figure 7-8   The Simplest Reversal Correction

Whenever you find an Internal Reversal it may be no
more than an electrolytic shift due to dehydration. The
simplest correction is to have your client drink an eight
ounce glass of clean water. This can readjust the electro-
lites. Afterward, test for the reversal.

Figure 7-9   Snapping the Fingers
                                        Internal Reversal Correction

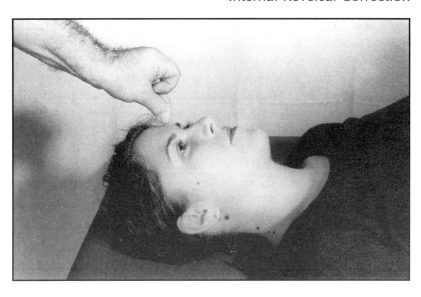

Figure 7-10   Tapping the Forehead
                                        Internal Reversal Correction

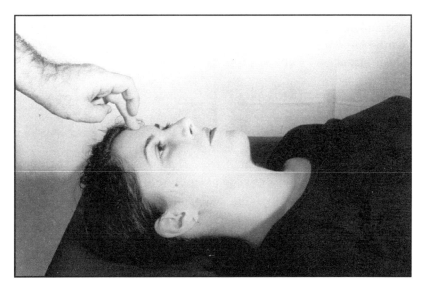

energies which are not fully integrated into the system and traveling in reverse of the system. This reverse energy flow confronts the forward moving energies causing blockages and imbalances. These *Retrograde Polarities* create mental, emotional, physical, and psychological instabilities. One of the key processes causing *Retrograde Polarities* is what is called the *Polarized Static Effect*. The *Polarized Static Effect* is generated by *"noise" or confusion in the "filters" disrupting the harmonious flow of energy.* The result is misdirected or miscommunicated energies. The filters include the five senses as well as individual consciousness and all of the experiences which have left a lasting effect. These, in turn, will affect the information that is coming in from as well as what is being interpreted by the individual in the environment, and what is going out into the environment. This indicates that there is a deletion and distortion of information. It is this deletion and distortion which causes the *Retrograde Polarities.*

There is another example of an incongruent response which you may encounter. This is when you have a weak response with a positive statement and a strong response with a negative statement.[2] What you will need to do here is to shift the responding so that you get a strong response with the positive statement and a weak response with the negative statement. You can accomplish this usually with a *Resource Realigning.*

You may want to test your client's differential responding to the problem state as well. To do this you can set up a series of possible *Retrograde Polarities.* What you will do is have your client make particular statements and test them. These statements will contain these words:

Want	Need	Allow	Accept
Able	Let	Permit	Desire
Willing	Approve of	Ready	Deserve

For example:
"I *allow* myself to be flexible in all areas of my life."
"I *refuse to allow* myself to be flexible in all areas of my life."

---

[2] This is called a *Simultaneous Incongruity* in Neuro-Linguistic Programming.

"I am *able* to be flexible in all areas of my life."
"I am *unable* to be flexible in all areas of my life."

"I *deserve* to be flexible in all areas of my life."
"I *deserve* to stay inflexible in all areas of my life."

These statements may also be phrased as:
"Think about *allowing* yourself to be flexible in all areas of your life."
"Think about *refusing to allow* yourself to be flexible in all areas of your life." and so forth.

The above will give you an idea of how to set up a series of statements to test for the *Retrograde Polarity.*

Many of us do not realize how a single word can produce an incongruent response in our unconscious. You can find, for example, that your client *wants* to be successful but does not feel that he *deserves* or *allows* it to happen. By realigning the resources of your client to be congruent in direction and motivation this can be what is needed for him to achieve his goal. First of all, you need to know what is holding him back and that is what you have done with your initial questioning. Then, working with the *Retrograde Polarities* you can find out what *single* energy pattern could be the culprit.

Besides a single word causing an incongruency a person can also connect a thought with a negative emotion. This could happen in the womb or outside of it in the early years of life. Then whenever the person entertains that particular thought, or a thought which is considered similar, the negative emotions are immediately triggered. In essence what we have is a feedback loop which continually reinforces itself holding the accompanying behaviors in place. (**Figure 7-11**) Thus, whenever there is this negative emotional charge being triggered in a situation there is stress thus creating an incongruent response.

The Pk technique bypasses the conscious mind's processes, rationalizations, ego defenses, and blocks. The theory behind it is that muscle testing can access imbalances, conflicts, and incongruities that are within the unconscious mind. Since there is a connection between the body and the mind you are using the body to get in touch with the unconscious of your client and tuning into the part(s) associated with or holding the energy for the specific problem in place. By asking questions or making statements in specific ways you can find the internal responding of your client. Then, by collecting the client's responses information is found which relates to the problem. It is possible that your client may experience some memories of past events due to these procedures. These may or may not be factual. In any case, using the infor-

Figure 7-11   Negative Emotion Feedback Loop

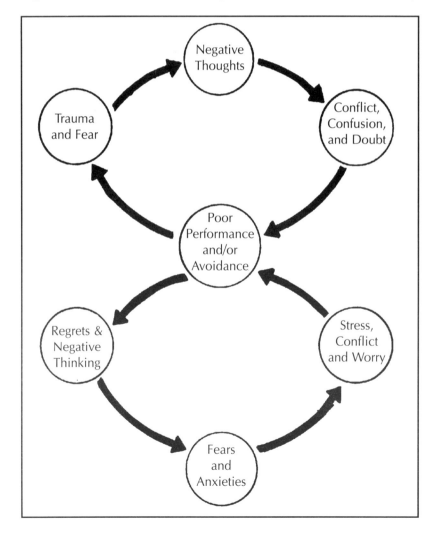

mation gathered as a *metaphor* allows your client to access information in a non-confrontational manner with little or no emotional catharsis.

The following are a series of *Retrograde Polarities* that you can use. There are two ways that you can use them: 1)You can begin by asking: "What issue needs to be cleared now?" What to do is to either go down with your hand from subject to subject testing as you go along; or 2) you may ask: "Is it from one to eleven?" "Twelve to twenty-three?" Then narrow it down to the specific issue for the present time through testing. Remember, your client's situation is unique and these can be of help. You will find it very useful to create statements that are specific for your client. The listed issues are:

1. Making Changes
2. Motivation
3. Flexibility
4. Clarity of Thinking
5. Staying in the Moment
6. Success
7. Prosperity
8. Working Smart Instead of Hard
9. Failure
10. Lack
11. Limitation
12. Loving Yourself
13. Loving Others
14. Attracting Loving Relationships
15. The Ending of a Relationship
16. Rejection
17. Control Issues
18. Self-Confidence
19. Giving up Self-Criticism
20. Need for Approval
21. Perfectionism
22. Procrastination
23. Self-Actualization

After you have found the issue for the session, turn to the appropriate subject and go through the statements checking which statements have a strong or a weak response.

"Think of ..."

1. Making Changes
    1. "... allowing yourself to make these changes."
        "... not allowing yourself to make these changes."
    2. "... making changes in your life."
        "... everything staying exactly the same."
    3. "... allowing yourself to make changes."
        "... not allowing yourself to make changes."
    4. "... accepting change as part of your life."
        "... not accepting change as part of your life."
    5. "... enjoying change as a part of your life."
        "... not enjoying change as a part of your life."
    6. "... feeling confident about changes occurring in your life."
        "... being afraid of any changes in your life."
    7. "... approving of changes in your life."
        "... not approving of changes in your life."
    8. "... being aligned and flowing easily with change."
        "... resisting change."
    9. "... acknowledging change working for you in your life."
        "... not acknowledging change working for you in your life."
    10. "... permitting change to operate for you in your life."
        "... not permitting change to operate for you in your life."

2. Motivation

   1. "... being motivated to making changes to accomplish your goals."

      "... staying the same and not having any motivation to accomplish your goals."

   2. "... making sure that you do things when they need to be done."

      "... procrastinating and putting off getting things done."

   3. "... doing what is necessary to become more motivated to achieve _____."

      "... having the same motivation as you have always had about achieving _____."

   4. "... having the drive and initiative to complete whatever you start."

      "... becoming disillusioned and disappointed and stopping doing whatever you start because you think you cannot do it."

   5. "... the joy of seeing your projects completed once started."

      "... feeling disappointed because the completion of your projects is so far off into the future."

   6. "... having the drive and determination to complete your projects once started."

      "... becoming tired and bored once you have begun a project."

   7. "... enjoying doing projects because of the pleasure you will have from accomplishing the project."

      "... doing projects and getting no pleasure from them."

   8. "... having the power, the impetus, and drive to accomplish your goals efficiently and effectively."

      "... your goals as being unattainable and unrealistic and that they cannot be done."

   9. "... being inspired to come up with new, creative, useful ideas that motivate you."

      "... doing the same old things over-and-over again."

10. "... having an exhilarating, creative imagination that comes up with useful and working ideas that inspire you to complete them."

"... having the same old ideas that promote the same old feelings."

11. "... having the drive, incentive, and inspiration to go beyond the limits you had."

"... staying the same."

12. "... being fully activated and motivated to making your goals reality."

"... approaching your goals the same way you have always done."

13. "... having the drive, motivation, and ambition to accomplish your goals easily and efficiently."

"... giving up your goals because they are too hard to get to."

14. "... having all of the energy and drive to complete your goals."

"... your goals as being difficult and hard to achieve."

15. "... being creatively motivated to have and accomplish your goals."

"... having no creative motivation and not accomplishing your goals."

16. "... being a creative problem-solver."

"... solving your problems in the same way you have always done."

17. "... being able to accomplish more in less time."

"... working the same as you have always done."

3. Flexibility
    1. "... having flexibility in all areas of your life."

        "... being rigid in your responses; not being free to respond and adapt well in most life situations."
    2. "... making the changes you need to become more flexible."

        "... being afraid to make these changes."
    3. "... being able to adapt and adjust well in life's situations."

        "... not being able to adapt or adjust well in life's situations."
    4. "... having a fluidity of adaptability."

        "... being rigid and restricted."
    5. "... having the ability to change your directions when necessary to insure a better outcome."

        "... being stuck in one direction and not being able to see any outcome other than the one planned."
    6. "... being able to accept another's point of view."

        "... being uncompromising when it comes to another's views."
    7. "... being able to respond appropriately, with intelligence, and wisdom to another's point if view."

        "... responding the same ways you have always done to another's point of view."
    8. "... being able to put yourself into another's place."

        "... being unable to take another's point of view."
    9. "... being able to adjust appropriately to each experience."

        "... being rigid and unable to adjust to each experience."
    10. "... being able to quickly bounce back from disappointment."

        "... disappointment being a long-lasting stumbling block."
    11. "... being able to respond appropriately to each experience."

        "... not responding in an appropriate manner to each experience."

4.   Clarity of Thinking

    1.   "... being able to see things as they are responding with clear and precise thoughts and actions."

       "... seeing things exactly the same way that you have always seen them and responding the same way as you have always done."

    2.   "... being able to clearly engage both your thinking and feeling processes to each experience."

       "... being 'stuck in your head' and limited and not accessing either your thinking or feelings as well as you could."

    3.   "... having that 'Aha!' experience often."

       "... thinking nothing new."

    4.   "... creative thoughts and ideas coming easily to you."

       "... creative thoughts and ideas being difficult to have."

    5.   "... having clear and precise thinking processes."

       "... your thinking being hazy and imprecise."

    6.   "... your thoughts being pure, elegant, and correct."

       "... your thoughts being confusing, clumsy, and scattered."

    7.   "... having connected, precise, and clear thinking processes."

       "... your thought processes being disconnected and confusing."

    8.   "... your thinking processes being polished, refined, and clear."

       "... your thinking processes being cluttered and inappropriate."

    9.   "... clearly seeing each experience as it is and responding appropriately."

       "... not being able to see each experience clearly nor respond appropriately."

   10.   "... your thoughts being precise and exact to each experience."

       "... your thoughts wandering imprecisely all the time."

   11.   "... being able to connect and associate thoughts, experiences, and ideas with amazing speed, regularity, skill, and joy."

       "... having the same old thoughts."

5. Staying in the Moment

   1. "... maintaining your awareness in the present; of being in the here-and-now."

   "... being stuck in the past or the future and not being in the present."

   2. "... being in the here-and-now as you are focused at each moment in time and point in space."

   "... having your mind constantly wander no matter where you are."

   4. "... being willing to learn positive things from every experience in time and space."

   "... time passing so quickly that you do not have time to learn from it."

   5. "... being able to concentrate on the moment that you are experiencing without losing track of the moment that has just passed."

   "... your concentration constantly fading from moment to moment so you lose track of where you are."

   6. "... your center of interest being in the here-and-now."

   "... you being easily distracted."

   7. "... your attention being concentrated at what you are doing at each moment in time."

   "... your attention not being concentrated at what you are doing at each moment in time."

   9. "... bringing all of your concentration to bear on the here-and-now."

   "... your concentration being scattered and unfocused."

  10. "... experiencing a one-ness with the present."

   "... feeling unconnected with the present."

  11. "... being able to savor each moment in time."

   "... being scattered and not having any focus at any time."

  12. "... being conscious of being focused on what is happening at each moment of time."

   "... your consciousness not being in each moment of time."

6. Success

    1. "... being a success in all you desire."

       "... being unsuccessful in fulfilling your desires."

    2. "... making the changes that you need in order to be successful."

       "... being unwilling to do anything to be more successful."

    3. "... welcoming success into your life."

       "... being afraid of the consequences of success."

    4. "... success being reachable and attainable."

       "... success as being unreachable and unattainable."

    5. "... success being an important part of your life."

       "... success as being difficult to achieve and hold on to."

    6. "... allowing your life to be successful."

       "... sabotaging your success."

    7. "... accepting the responsibilities that accompany success."

       "... not accepting or taking the responsibilities that accompany success ."

    8. "... attracting the most supportive people and conditions that contribute to your success."

       "... not being able to attract anyone that can contribute to your success."

    9. "... being motivated toward being successful."

       "... having no motivation and fearing success."

   10. "... being able to see and create many possibilities for being successful."

       "... not being able to see and creating any possibilities for being successful."

   11. "... confidently welcoming success."

       "... being afraid of success."

   12. "... attracting successful events and people everywhere you go."

       "... attracting unsupportive people in your successful endeavors."

13. "... being able to _____ and initiate new and creative ways to become successful."

    "... not being creative and having everything staying the same."

14. "... acting quickly and appropriately to achieve success."

    "... procrastinating and waiting too long to take action to achieve success."

15. "... life being enjoyable and happy and success being easily achievable."

    "... life being a struggle with success being always out of reach."

16. "... achieving success as being fun and easy."

    "... achieving success as being a constant struggle."

17. "... being able to achieve and enjoy your success."

    "... success being difficult to achieve and hold on to."

18. "... success as the result of working smart."

    "... success being difficult no matter how hard you work."

19. "... coming up with new workable ideas that make your work easier."

    "... continuing to work with ineffective methods and getting disappointing results."

20. "... doing the best and most effective things to achieve success."

    "... acting out of desperation and doing anything to be successful."

18. "... the joy of achieving the goals you set out to do."

    "... the struggle to get even your most simple goals."

7. Prosperity

    1. "... being prosperous in everything you do."

        "... being as prosperous as you have always been."

    2. "... making the changes that you need in order attract prosperity."

        "... not doing anything to change and attract prosperity."

    3. "... attracting prosperity everywhere you go."

        "... prosperity always being out of reach."

    4. "... prosperity being easily attainable."

        "... prosperity being hard to get."

    5. "... being a magnet for prosperity."

        "... repelling prosperity."

    6. "... attracting the most appropriate people and conditions to insure your being prosperous."

        "... prosperous people and conditions not being attracted to you."

    7. "... being able to find new and creative ways of attracting prosperity."

        "... doing the same things you have always done and not attracting prosperity."

    8. "... welcoming prosperity with open arms."

        "... being afraid of being prosperous."

    9. "... prosperity as your birthright."

        "... prosperity as being there for someone else but not for you."

    10. "... having all the money that you need and more."

        "... having less money than you need and desire."

    11. "... prosperity as being fun, enjoyable, and easy to attain."

        "... prosperity as hard to get and you worry that you cannot attain it."

    12. "... being able to plan and achieve prosperity in easy steps."

        "... achieving prosperity as a struggle with difficult steps that you cannot do."

13. "... having and enjoying your prosperity."

   "... the feeling that no matter how prosperous you are it is never enough."

14. "... prosperity as being the result an attitude of working smart."

   "... prosperity as being the result of many difficulties and very hard work that you do not want to do."

15. "... having prosperity as being the result of intelligent planning, focused intent, and clear goals."

   "... the lack of prosperity as being the result of many difficulties and plain 'bad luck.'"

8. Working Smart Instead of Hard
    1. "... being able to work smart instead of hard."

        "... working hard instead of smart."

    2. "... being able to make work easy and fun."

        "... work being a long, hard, and difficult chore."

    3. "... making the changes necessary to be able to work smarter instead of harder."

        "... being unable to change so work remains hard."

    4. "... work being a challenge to use your talents and abilities more fully."

        "... work being a bore where your talents are wasted."

    5. "... having creative, new, and exciting ways of working smart and better."

        "... not finding any ways to be creative in work."

    6. "... being able to come up with new and efficient ways to make work easier and better."

        "... work being...work."

    7. "... seeing work as exciting, easy, and pleasant."

        "... continuing to see work as dull, difficult, and hard."

9. Failure
    1. "... being successful."
       "... being a failure."
    2. "... failing as a means of reorganization and going on."
       "... failing as the end of a path."
    3. "... failing as a way to learn what not to do."
       "... failing as something being impossible."
    4. "... failing as part of life's learning experiences."
       "... failing as disappointing and limiting."
    5. "... failing as part of problem-solving."
       "... failing as creating more problems."
    6. "... failing as an opportunity for growth."
       "... failing as restricting your growth."
    7. "... failing as temporary."
       "... failing as permanent."
    8. "... failing as a set-back that you can overcome."
       "... failing as an obstruction you cannot get around."
    9. "... failing as telling you something about a choice you have made."
       "... failing as telling you there is something lacking in yourself."
    10. "... failing as not being successful at one thing."
        "... failing as not being able to achieve anything."
    11. "... failing as helping you to learn more about yourself in positive, constructive ways."
        "... failing as an indication of your own inferiority."
    12. "... failing as telling you that you simply made an error in judgement."
        "... failing as a total defeat for yourself and your choices."
    13. "... failing as telling you you are not successful at one thing."
        "... failure as telling you you are ineffective as a person."

10. Lack

  1. "... having what you need when you need it."

      "... not being able to make ends meet."

  2. "... being able to find creative, constructive ways to prosper in whatever you do."

      "... times being difficult and hard and always coming up short."

  3. "... having the "golden touch."

      "... living from hand-to-mouth."

  4. "... having a consciousness for wealth and success."

      "... having a consciousness for lack and failure."

  5. "... coming up with creative, constructive ideas to make your life easier and fun."

      "... having the same old ideas you have always had and getting the same things you have always gotten."

  6. "... having the ability to be at the right place at the right time to attract riches."

      "... floundering and attracting lack and poverty."

  7. "... having the consciousness for creating affluence."

      "... having the consciousness for creating lack and limitation."

  8. "... being a magnet for wealth and success."

      "... repelling wealth and success."

  9. "... being able to take care of all of your expenses and still have a lot of money left over to have fun."

      "... barely making ends meet and having nothing left over for yourself."

11. Limitation

   1. "... being unlimited in thought and action."

      "... being repressed and constricted in thought and action."

   2. "... being free to make your own choices."

      "... having to wait for others' approval before choosing."

   3. "... accepting the responsibility of being unlimited in creative thought and action."

      "... not wanting the responsibility of unlimited creative thought and action."

   4. "... being free to choose your own course of action."

      "... having to wait until others decide before you make your choices."

   5. "... feeling free to express your thoughts, ideas, and actions."

      "... feeling confined, restricted, and repressed."

   6. "... feeling free to love yourself and others."

      "... restricting your love for yourself and others."

   7. "... coming up with new, exciting, useful thoughts and ideas."

      "... having the same old limiting thoughts and ideas."

   8. "... your past being a learning experience for present and future growth."

      "... your past being a block and limiting future growth."

   9. "... learning from the past in order to create a future full of happiness and success."

      "... being lost in the past and afraid of the future."

  10. "... the future being made from your present choices."

      "... the future as being dependent on someone else."

  11. "... freely expressing yourself and who you are."

      "... being afraid of expressing yourself and who you are."

12. Loving Yourself

1. "... being able to love yourself even though you make mistakes."

    "... not loving yourself because you cannot do everything right."

2. "... your own needs, wants, and desires as important."

    "... other's needs, wants, and desires as more important than yours."

3. "... being loving and supportive of yourself."

    "... being unloving to and critical of yourself."

4. "... taking good care of your body."

    "... taking care of your body as you have always done."

5. "... taking good care of yourself."

    "... being the same as you have always been to yourself."

6. "... looking after yourself first without being egocentric."

    "... looking out for others at the expense of your own well-being."

7. "... being in tune with your own needs, wants, and desires."

    "... being out of touch with your own needs, wants, and desires."

8. "... it being okay to consider your own needs, wants, and desires."

    "... others' needs, wants, and desires as more important than your own."

13. Loving Others

   1. "... seeing others as being worthy of being loved."

     "... seeing others as being unworthy of love."

   2. "... seeing others as human beings who do not always do the right thing."

     "... seeing others as unworthy and undeserving of love because of what they do."

   3. "... self-respect as necessary to respecting others."

     "... others being more important than yourself."

   4. "... respecting others' points of view."

     "... others' point of view being less important than yours."

   5. "... extending simple courtesies to others."

     "... being courteous only to certain people."

   6. "... giving others the same respect you want from them."

     "... not giving others the same respect you want from them."

   7. "... 'Doing unto others as you would have them do unto you.'"

     "... demanding others respect you no matter what."

   8. "... loving others even though they make mistakes or bad choices."

     "... not caring for others because they do not do things right."

14. Attracting Loving Relationships

1. "... being attracted to loving, caring, supportive people."

    "... being attracted to unloving, uncaring, nonsupportive people."

2. "... being able to attract loving, caring, supportive people."

    "... attracting unloving, uncaring, unsupportive people."

3. "... attracting open, honest, and concerned people."

    "... attracting people who tell me what I want to hear."

4. "... being honest and open in your relationships."

    "... being dishonest and secretive in your relationships."

5. "... being able to honestly express yourself openly and honestly in your relationships."

    "... expressing yourself dishonestly and deceitfully in your relationships."

6. "... having many meaningful relationships."

    "... having meaningless relationships."

7. "... being able to recognize and respond appropriately to insincere and dishonest people."

    "... being manipulated by insincere and dishonest people."

8. "... being able to love yourself in meaningful ways."

    "... loving others more than yourself."

9. "... allowing others to be themselves."

    "... having to be in control of your relationships."

10. "... your relationships being a harmony of give-and-take."

    "... your relationships being a battle of mostly giving or mostly taking."

11. "... seeing your relationships for what they are."

    "... being blinded by your own biases in your relationships."

12. "... being able to appropriately respond emotionally in your relationships."

    "... not being able to appropriately respond emotionally in your relationships."

13. "... attracting loving, meaningful relationships."

"... attracting critical and/or abusive relationships."

14. "... being yourself in your meaningful relationships."

"... not being or expressing yourself in your meaningful relationships."

15. "... allowing others in your meaningful relationships the freedom to express themselves."

"... not allowing others the freedom to express themselves in your meaningful relationships."

16. "... being loveable."

"... being unloveable."

17. "... being able to attract loving, caring, supportive relationships."

"... attracting the same relationships as you have always done."

18. "... being able to accept others in spite of their failings."

"... being disappointed in others when they do not live up to where you have put them."

19. "... perceiving and promoting the relationships that you intuitively know are the best for you."

"... promoting the worst relationships you can have by being caring, loving, and attentive to those people who take advantage of you."

20. "... allowing yourself to be yourself in your meaningful relationships."

"... not allowing yourself to be who you are in your meaningful relationships."

21. "... the joy of learning about yourself through your meaningful relationships."

"... not being able to learn anything about yourself through your meaningful relationships."

22. "... being able to see yourself in others through your meaningful relationships."

"... being blinded by and not being able to see yourself in your meaningful relationships."

23. "... being able to intuitively know those with whom to have the best relationships."

"... attracting the same kinds of relationships as you have always done."

24. "... loving yourself in positive, constructive ways."

"... not being able to love yourself."

25. "... being able to accept others regardless of the choices they make."

"... being disappointed and hurt when others make choices that you are unhappy with."

15. The Ending of a Relationship

    1. "... a relationship ending as a change in the direction of the relationship."

    "... a relationship ending as him/her abandoning you."

    2. "... a relationship ending as a way of finding something about the choices you are making in relationships."

    "... a relationship ending as being told you are not good enough."

    3. "... a relationship ending as a means of taking care of yourself."

    "... a relationship ending as a forsaking and rejecting of you."

    4. "... a relationship ending as a means of evaluating your self-concern."

    "... a relationship ending as embarrassing and humiliating."

    5. "... a relationship ending as a way of learning positive new things about yourself."

    "... a relationship ending as a way of proving you are a failure."

    6. "... a relationship ending as a way of positively learning about others."

    "... a relationship ending as a way of reinforcing the idea that others will always desert you."

16. Rejection

1. "... feeling good about yourself regardless of others criticizing you."

"... taking other's criticism to heart and feeling as if there is something wrong with you."

2. "... accepting yourself even when others put you down."

"... feeling rejected and dejected when others put you down."

3. "... taking others' criticism and using it as a learning experience."

"... others' criticism as being an indication of your own inabilities and limitations."

4. "... being able to positively and creatively use others' disapproval to make changes."

"... having to need other's approval at all times."

5. "... seeing clearly what is behind the disapproval or rejection of others."

"... being controlled by others' disapproval or rejection."

6. "... others' disapproval or rejection as a means of understanding them."

"... others' disapproval or rejection as them telling you something's wrong in you."

7. "... the disapproval or criticism of others as a way of creatively improving what you are doing."

"... the disapproval or criticism of others as telling you that you are wrong and doing nothing about it."

8. "... sticking by your choices even if others disapprove."

"... letting others' disapproval be important in your choices."

17. Control Issues
1. "... allowing yourself the freedom to express yourself in all of your relationships."

   "... not expressing yourself in any of your relationships."
2. "... allowing others the freedom to express themselves."

   "... not allowing others the freedom to express themselves."
3. "... being flexible, allowing others the freedom to be themselves."

   "... having to be in control of others all of the time."
4. "... accepting yourself for who you are."

   "... feeling you have to be or act differently than you feel."
5. "... being an independent and creative thinker coming up with unique and useful ideas."

   "... being limited and controlled in your thinking."
6. "... being flexible and accepting of life's experiences."

   "... everything having to be the way you want it."
7. "... accepting people for who they are."

   "... people having to be what you want them to be."
8. "... allowing others to be who they are."

   "... others having to live up to your expectations."
9. "... allowing yourself the freedom to make mistakes."

   "... having to do the right thing all of the time."
10. "... accepting your own human falibilities."

    "... not accepting your human falibilities."
11. "... effectively being able to take care of the majority of life's situations that you encounter."

    "... feeling fearful and helpless to take care of life's situations as they come up."
12. "... being able to use your talents and abilities creatively and effectively."

    "... having your talents and abilities restricted because of the situations you encounter."
13. "... being able to independently and clearly see, evaluate, and choose the most appropriate courses of action to solve problems."

    "... feeling helpless and confused as to a course of action to solve problems."

18. Self-Confidence
  1. "... having confidence in yourself and your abilities."

     "... not being confident in what you can do or in expressing your talents and abilities."
  2. "... making the changes you need to be more self-confident."

     "... not building more self-confidence."
  3. "... believing in yourself and your ideas."

     "... letting others tell you that you can or cannot do something."
  4. "... following your inner convictions."

     "... following the same path as you have always done."
  5. "... having the faith and certainty to accomplish your goals."

     "... having no faith or certainty to accomplish any goals."
  6. "... being sure of yourself and what you want to accomplish."

     "... being unsure of yourself and what you want to accomplish."
  7. "... having the courage and confidence to take a risk to express yourself and your abilities."

     "... playing it safe."
  8. "... taking responsibility for being in charge of your life."

     "... not taking the responsibility for being in charge of your life."
  9. "... being balanced, harmonious, and self-assuredly in control of yourself."

     "... being out of balance and out of control."
  10. "... having a confident presence of mind so you can accomplish what you set out to do."

      "... lacking confidence or presence of mind so that you can keep things as they are."
  11. "... being sure of doing what you set out to do."

      "... being uncertain of doing anything once you begin."
  12. "... knowing what you want to do and going for it."

      "... wondering what you want to do and where you want to go."
  13. "... finding and knowing your life's work."

      "... being and doing the same work as you have always done and feeling you are not expressing your full potential."

19. Giving up Self-Criticism

1. "... giving yourself praise for the things that you do."

   "... not praising yourself for anything."

2. "... not coming down on yourself when you make a mistake."

   "... coming down on yourself hard everytime you make a mistake."

3. "... making the changes necessary to give up self-criticism."

   "... continuing your self-criticism."

4. "... speaking with love and respect to yourself."

   "... harshly criticizing yourself whenever you make a mistake."

5. "... paying attention to what you are saying to yourself about yourself."

   "... not speaking to yourself with any respect or concern."

6. "... speaking to yourself with respect and care."

   "... speaking to yourself disrespectfully and without consideration."

7. "... approving of the choices that you make and the things you do."

   "... putting yourself down whenever something does not work out quite as you had planned."

8. "... seeing the good in what you do even if it does not work out."

   "... finding fault with everything you do whether it works out or not."

9. "... looking for what works in whatever does not succeed and finding ways of making it work."

   "... nit-picking every detail of what does not succeed and doing nothing about making changes."

20. Need for Approval

1. "... feeling good about whatever you accomplish regardless of other's approval."

    "... needing others tell you that what you are doing is okay."

2. "... others' criticism as a way of making what you are doing better."

    "... others' criticism as the way things should be."

3. "... you creating your own value or worth."

    "... others' opinions of you as being your value or worth."

4. "... valuing yourself and your own needs."

    "... the needs of others being more important than your own."

5. "... self-respect as being a high priority."

    "... others' opinions of you being the highest priority."

6. "... regarding significant others with respect."

    "... significant others being more important than you by idolizing them."

7. "... enjoying the choices that you make and the things you accomplish."

    "... waiting for others to tell you that you are 'OK' after you have done something."

8. "... others' failures as a learning experience for you."

    "... others' failures as a warning that you cannot do many things."

9. "... feeling confident in who you are."

    "... others' praise making you feel good about who you are."

21. Perfectionism

  1. "... giving constructive suggestions to others that help them improve what they do."

     "... criticizing what others do."

  2. "... accepting people for who they are."

     "... criticizing and downing people because they do not live up to your expectations."

  3. "... accepting situations for what they are."

     "... finding fault and blaming others for situations that do not fit your expectations."

  4. "... allowing people to be themselves."

     "... seeing people in rigid, biased ways."

  5. "... accepting the imperfections in life."

     "... everything having to be perfect or you cannot accept it."

  6. "... having a generous attitude toward life's experiences."

     "... being petty and finicky about whatever does not seem to be as it should be to you."

  7. "... being able to adjust and flow with life's ups and downs."

     "... being rigid and inflexible in your approach to life."

  8. "... accepting your own fallibility."

     "... accepting your own infallibility."

  9. "... being tolerant of others choices and actions."

     "... being intolerant of others because they are not up to your standards."

  10. "... being open and accepting of other people's choices and actions."

     "... having to have everyone act as you want them."

  11. "... accepting the fact that nothing is perfect."

     "... expecting everything to be perfect."

  12. "... communicating with others in an open, honest, and tolerant way."

     "... talking down to others in a dogmatic, critical way."

13. "... allowing yourself to make mistakes and profiting from those mistakes."

"... thinking of yourself as 'mistake-proof' and that mistakes show one's inferiority."

14. "... learning something from everybody."

"... you know everything and cannot learn anything from anyone else."

15. "... allowing others to express their thoughts and feelings openly."

"... restricting others' expressing their thoughts and feelings."

16. "... being accepting of others' wants and needs and helping others achieve them."

"... seeing to it that your own wants and needs are taken care of irrespective of others'."

17. "... allowing yourself the freedom to be flexible."

"... being rigid and dogmatic."

18. "... being able to accept and find humor in your mistakes."

"... taking yourself too seriously."

19. "... being able to accept life as it is."

"... taking life too seriously."

20. "... accepting the fact that no one is perfect."

"... expecting others to live up to intolerable standards."

21. "... allowing others to live out their life as they see fit."

"... being prejudiced against others because they are not living life as they should."

22. "... being able to enjoy your own falibilites."

"... never making mistakes."

23. "... growing with your relationships."

"... your relationships being what you want or not at all."

24. "... seeing to yourself in a non-egocentric way."

"... seeing yourself as the most important person in the world."

22. Procrastination
1. "... doing a job when it needs to be done."

"... waiting and not getting a job done at all."

2. "... staying with a particular job until it is completed."

"... becoming bored and side-tracked on a job and continually putting it off."

3. "... the excitement of succeeding at a job that you start."

"... becoming disillusioned and not completing what you start."

4. "... finding a lot of good reasons to begin, continue, and finish a job."

"... making excuses for not beginning a job."

5. "... getting a job done right the first time."

"... making excuses for not doing the job right."

6. "... being focused on whatever job you start."

"... constantly having your mind wander whenever you are doing a job so you do not complete it."

7. "... finding exciting new ways of doing things and doing things in new exciting ways."

"... putting things off because you are bored having to do things the same way."

8. "... finding excitement in getting things done so you can move on to doing new things."

"... not wanting to get one thing done because you will have to do something else later."

9. "... enjoying being active and getting whatever you set out to do completed and completed well."

"... being inactive and either not completing or not completing well what you set out to do."

10. "... having pride in completing all you begin."

"... not caring if you complete anything you start."

23. Self-Actualization

1. "... being able to see what is honest and true in people and experiences."

   "... being taken-in by phony and fake things and people in life."

2. "... dealing with unpleasant situations rather than escaping into some fantasy life."

   "... running away from life's unpleasant situations rather than dealing with them."

3. "... accepting yourself and your own imperfections."

   "... not being accepting of your imperfections and shortcomings."

4. "... acting appropriately in emotional situations."

   "... over-reacting in emotional situations."

5. "... focusing on problems and finding solutions."

   "... being focused on yourself or on the problem instead of on finding a solution."

6. "... devoting the attention that you need to the task at hand."

   "... being self-conscious and seeing yourself as the problem in any problem situation."

7. "... seeking and enjoying private moments of personal solitude."

   "... having to need others around all of the time."

8. "... using private moments to concentrate on things of special interest."

   "... private moments being periods of boredom and frustration."

9. "... being an independent thinker."

   "... having to have others' approval."

10. "... being yourself in the face of rejection and unpopularity."

    "... feeling that there is something wrong with you whenever you are rejected."

11. "... pursuing your own personal interests even when others reject you."

    "... bowing to others' opinions."

12. "... maintaining your personal integrity even when others reject you."

"... compromising yourself when others reject you."

13. "... appreciating the good and simple things in life."

"... not 'stopping to smell the roses.'"

14. "... seeing the uniqueness of the commonplace experiences of life."

"... the commonplace being boring and not worth your time."

15. "... enjoying each experience for what it is."

"... having to categorize each experience."

16. "... enjoying the one-ness of nature and each experience."

"... having to be told what is real and what is not."

17. "... feeling as if you belong to humanity as a whole."

"... having to belong to a group or organization."

18. "... being concerned with what affects all living things on this planet."

"... being concerned only with yourself and your own immediate experience."

19. "... having a few very trusted and loving friends whom you can confide in and experience life with."

"... having to have a lot of people around you that you have to call 'friend.'"

20. "... loving people for who they are."

"... restricting your experience of others by categorizing them."

21. "... making the choices and doing the things you do because they are universally ethical and moral."

"... having to adhere to convention and doing what you do because you are supposed to by law."

22. "... finding the humor in the absurdities of life and in words, puns, and so on."

"... laughing at people and their problems, misfortunes, or cruelties."

23. "... being creative and inventive in many of life's situations."

"... being totally conventional in handling life's situations."

24. "... being independent in thought and choice so you can see the inconsistencies in society."

"... allowing yourself to be manipulated and controlled by the society."

25. "... having the ability to see yourself, others, and the world in such a way that it leads to self-awareness."

"... being blinded by social convention, others, and what is going on in the world so you cannot become more self-aware."

26. "... accepting yourself for who you are."

"... not being able to accept yourself for who you are."

27. "... accepting others for who they are."

"... not accepting others for who they are."

28. "... standing up for the things that make life worth living."

"... not standing up for the things that make life worth living."

29. "... being able to see new possibilities in situations and acting on those possibilities."

"... seeing things in restricted and unproductive ways."

30. "... being open to the possibilities of new personal growth."

"... not seeing any possibilities for any personal growth."

31. "... allowing yourself to make mistakes and to profit from those mistakes."

"... not allowing yourself to make mistakes nor learning from the mistakes you make."

CHAPTER 8

IN DEPTH INFORMATION GATHERING

You have tested your client and s/he is responding correctly. You have tested for *Retrograde Polarities* and you have found several. The next step is to find out if you have enough information to do a *Resource Realigning*.

The process of finding out if you have enough information is quite simple. You have your client place one hand palm down on her forehead and ask: "Yes or no. Can this be cleared now?" and test. **(Figure 8-1)** If you receive a "yes" response then go directly into the *Resource Realigning*. If you receive a "no" response, which is most likely, then you will need to gather more information. With a no response there are a number of things that you can do in order to gather more information and many of them can give some fascinating results. It is also wise to restate each piece of information that you get and check your client's reaction to it.

Here is where you will need to think in a more expansive manner. You can question and test beginning with the most obvious and go on from there. A beginning test can start with this question: "Yes or no, is this (problem state) held in place with an emotion? Hold." The chances are very high that you will get a "yes" response. With a "yes" response you need to find which emotion is holding the problem state in place. The standard line of questioning is:

"Is this emotion *fear* or something related to fear?"

"Is this emotion *anger* or something related to anger?"

"Is this emotion *anxiety* or something related to anxiety?"

Figure 8-1

With Your Client's Hand on Her Forehead ask,
"Can this be cleared now?" and test.

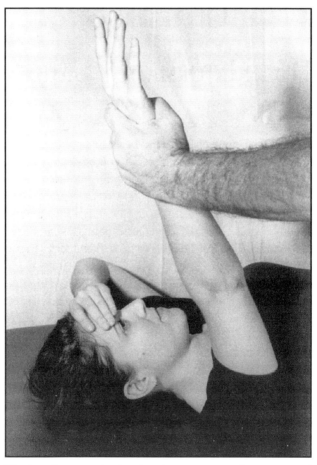

The hand across the forehead is activating the emotional
points over the forehead. You will be able to find out very
quickly if the information that you have uncovered is
enough to break the pattern that has been occurring in
your client's life-style.

"Is this emotion *helplessness* or something related to helplessness?"

"Is this emotion about *vulnerability* or something related to vulnerability?"

"Is this emotion *guilt* or something related to guilt?"

"Is this emotion *hurt* or something related to emotional hurt?"

"Is this emotion a *personal demand* or something related to a personal demand?"

"Is this emotion a *demand on another* or something related to a demand on another?"

"Is this emotion a *demand on the world* or something related to a demand on the world?"

You may be able to come up with another question or two yourself that you can test. These questions will cover the vast majority of cases.

After you have found what the blocking emotion is you can again question to find out if that is enough information. The chances are, it is not. So, you will need to continue.

The next step is to determine whose emotion it is. Ask: "Yes or no, is this emotion your (or you can use the client's name) emotion? Hold." If you get an affirmative response then check again to see if you have enough information to clear. If you have a negative response then ask: "Yes or no, is this emotion the *mother's* emotion? Hold." If you receive a negative response then you know that it's the opposite parent. You may want to question just in case anyway. Then, again, inquire to find if that is enough information. One thing to remember, even if you do find out that the emotion was originally someone else's emotion it still belongs to your client now. By finding out what the emotion is you will be able to bring it out so that your client can take ownership of it. Once this has occurred then it can be more easily dealt with.

Another emotional check that you can add to your repertoire is those associated with *Demand States*. These demand states will be placed on ourself, others, or the world. We will know these states with the use of the words *would, should, have to, need to, must, can't,* or *I can't stand it* or an emotional internal or external tone of voice. These words also indicate perfectionism. You may want to check these words in reference to the problem state as well. Quite often we will make demands of ourself which are unreasonable, unrealistic, and irrational. These demands are used to instill more feelings of disappointment, disillusionment, and failure. We set ourself up for failure purposely and do not realize it. When we make demands of others which are also unreasonable, unrealistic, and irrational we will never tell them or we will indirectly tell them expecting the other to know exactly what we want and mean.Then when the expectations are not fulfilled we will become disappointed, disillusioned, and often feel that there's something wrong with us. With demands on the world we expect the world to meet our unreasonable standards. When it does not we become disappointed, disillusioned and, often times, fearful.

Assuming that you need to continue, the next level of questioning for information is to find the *Time of Origin* of the problem state. This is a most important part and most unique aspect of Pk. The most effective method of doing this is to have your client place his/her hand across the forehead and ask: "Yes or no, was there an original time for this problem? Hold." With a positive response continue by stating: "Think of (problem state). Go back to the *Time of Origin* of this problem state. (Tap the *Thymus Point* [**Figure 8-2**]) Was this problem state present ___ years ago? Hold." You will most likely get a strong response. This strong response indicates that it existed at that point.

Figure 8-2   Tapping the Thymus for
                         Time Reversal and Projection

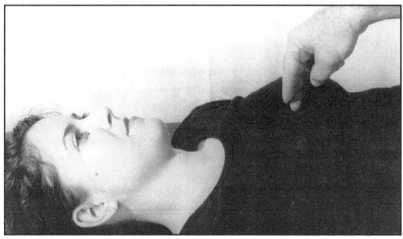

Once you have that response, again tap the *Thymus Point* and state: "Go back ___ years. Was this problem state present ___ years ago? Hold." Continue going back tapping the *Thymus Point* until you get a weak response. When you get a weak response that will indicate that the problem did not exist at that point. By doing this process you can get to the precise year or age of the origin of the problem state. If the time indicated is within a memory range ask your client if she can recall anything that may have occurred around that time. She may, or may not, recall something.

You may come to a point in time when you receive a weak response and it is not the *Time of Origin* of the problem state. Go on. Ask if you have enough information to clear the problem state. There is a possibility that you will get a positive response. Clear it. After the clearing, have your client place her hand on her forehead and state: "*This one* is healed," and test. You will most likely get a strong response. Then state: "There's more to do on *that one*," and test. Here you will get a strong response. When this happens it means that you have most likely encountered the *Time of Awareness* of the problem state. When this happens simply ask: "Yes or no. Do we need to go back farther to get the *Time of Origin* of this problem state? Hold." You will receive a strong response. If you receive a weak response the chances arc you are working with a problem state that the unconscious does not need to deal with immediately or that you need to do some specific testing on. The best thing to do is to then go back to the emotions and clear the emotion underlying the problem state. By clearing the underlying emotion you can get to the problem state from another angle. You will be able to get at the *Time of Origin* easier after that.

There are a number of problems an individual can have which may have occurred in utero. When going back in utero tap the *Thymus Point* and state: "Go back to birth. Was this problem present at birth? Hold." If you receive a strong response you will need to go back farther. The next step is to tap the *Thymus Point* and state: "Go back to conception. Was this problem present at conception? Hold." Assuming that you receive a weak response then you will go trimester-by-trimester and can come to the month when the problem originated. Once you have the month ask your client if she knows what may have occurred during this time. Sometimes she will know because it may be common knowledge in the family. It really is not necessary if she knows or not or even if she wants to discuss it. The *Resource Realigning* will still clear it.

At this point have your client place her hand on her forehead again and ask: "Do we have enough information to clear this now? Hold." The chances are, you will receive a positive response.

Let us assume that you have a strong response at conception. The next question is to ask: "Do we need to go farther back? Hold." With a positive response to this question you will be going back into *genetic inheritance*. In other words, the problem may be a *family pattern* that has continued unchecked. In order to find this pattern you need only to do exactly as you have been; tap the *Thymus Point* each time and ask: "Was this problem 1 generation in the past? Hold." "Was this problem ___ generations in the past? Hold." and so on until you receive a weak response. Continue going back into the past to find the generation when the problem originated. It is obvious that going back into genetic inheritance your client will not have any information about what happened. So, as soon as you find the generation stop and clear it. Again, have your client place her hand on her forehead and ask if there is enough information to clear the problem state.

One thing that needs to be addressed here is the fact that researchers have concluded that some of our values, attitudes, and behavioral predispositions *are genetically inherited*. With the more than twenty years of twin studies it has been found that there is a 50/50 relationship between heredity and environment in reference to our personality. That is, 50 percent of our personality is inherited and 50 percent is learned. Just what is inherited and what is learned is not really known. Those portions of our personality which are learned and which are interfering with our life will be easily seen with the *Time Reversal Procedure*. Those things which are apparently inherited and the generation of their origin are assumed through the same process.

The theory behind the *Time Reversal Procedure* is that the unconscious knows the *Time of Origin* of a problem. So, by thinking about the problem state and asking the physical body the unconscious can bring out the correct time. As far as going into genetic inheritance, it is assumed that the DNA patterns are accessible by the unconscious and that the DNA can be altered. It is a "genetic therapy" of sorts. It is also assumed that this genetic therapy is *generative*. That is, once cleared the changed DNA pattern can be brought up to the present and will continue to cause other changes in that person's life.

The fact is the *Time Reversal Procedure* going into genetic inheritance may be nothing more than a metaphor. One thing to remember is that metaphors trigger unconscious processes. Consequently, even if it is a metaphor it is a metaphor that seems to work quite well.

After you have gathered all of the information that is appropriate the best thing that you can do is to restate or summarize the information. This allows the conscious mind to catch up with the unconscious and conscious processes can be brought into play with the change.

Another direction that you can go is to check the *Emotional Reflex Points* on the body. (**Figure 8-3**) The *Emotional Reflex Points*, as you can see, correspond to specific organs. When checking these points you *aim* your fingers at each point (**Figure 8-4)** and tell your client to: "Think of (problem state). Hold," while having her continue to hold. At one of the points you will get a weak response. When this happens you have the organ which is being affected by the problem state. You can then clear the organ and the problem state will be cleared at the same time.

Before discussing the different organs and their effects on emotions and behavior, an understanding of the word *energy* that was used earlier needs to be considered. It is necessary to have a better comprehension of what energy is and how it is used and understood in *Psychokinesiology*.

In general, energy is the capacity or power to produce an effect. In the very technical sense, energy is a property of a system which is a measure of its capacity for doing work. Work is basically defined as what is done when a force moves its point of application. Energy is the potential or power that causes that movement. It comes in a variety of forms: electrical, heat, chemical, nuclear, mechanical, as well as other types and forms.

What you are working with in Pk is the *electrochemical energy* that is within the body. One of the things you need to remember is that the body is an electrochemical system and the brain and the nervous system operate electrochemically. All of our thoughts, our experiences, and our emotions are made up of this electrochemical energy. Whenever a thought, an emotion, or an idea becomes fixated at a point or an experience in time, the energy that is contained within the experience and the emotion itself will continue as long as the individual holds on to the thought and the emotion. Once it is released then the individual does not have to pay much attention to it because he does not have to deal with it. The problem is that most of the time whenever we have experiences our whole system gets involved in it: visual, auditory, feeling states on

Figure 8-3

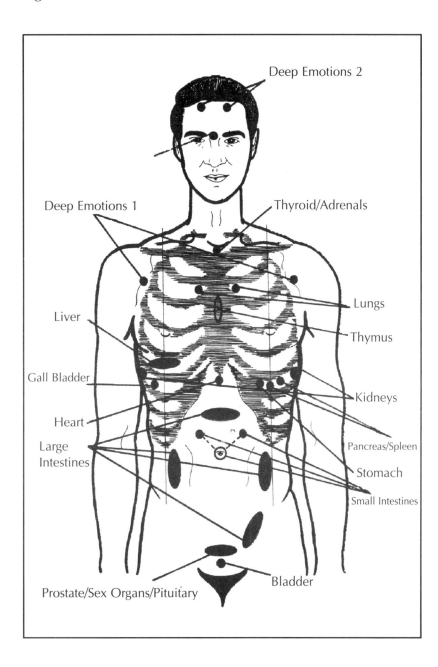

Figure 8-4   Aiming the Hand at the
                                              Emotional Reflex Points

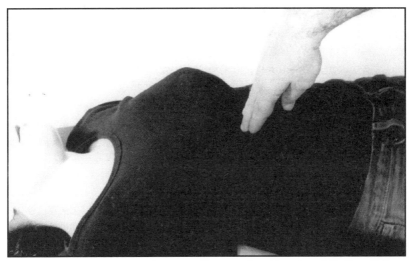

It is not necessary to touch your client on her Emotional Reflex Points.
Simply aim at the point you're checking.

and within the body, as well as olfactory and gustatory. The experiences
that we adhere to are the ones that are going to affect our system the
most. Consequently, when they are affecting our thinking and our emotions they are affecting the whole energy flow throughout the body.

An emotion does not just affect us mentally. Whenever we are holding on to an emotion or a thought consistently it is also affecting us
physically. This is why after many years of holding on to a particular
thought, idea, or emotion actual physical problems occur in the body. It
is interesting that our language itself shows us where the problems are
going to be. Statements like: "Something is eating at my craw," "I wish
that _____ would get off of my back," "I can't stomach hearing that
anymore." It is statements like this when are consistently repeated, the
thought, the idea, the emotions which surround that statement, then
keep our whole system functioning at that point *as if* we have never gotten away from it.

What *Psychokinesiology* does is get into the unconscious. Pk is able to get under those emotions, thoughts, and ideas and is able to release them and free them so that the potential of the individual is released. The more that you hold on to a thought, an idea, or an emotion the less chance there is of that energy being released. What happens is that you have less and less of a chance of achieving the goals that you want because there is something underlying the possible change.

Human beings have a beautiful automatic process called *generalization*. Generalization helps us to keep a stable and predictable world. It is a process by which we assume that certain experiences are *similar* even though they may not be. There may be similar *properties* leading to them or in them but they are not comparable. The fact of the matter is once you have had an experience it is finished. The generalization is the process that helps us to learn from the experience. If we learn from the experience then we will be generalizing the learning. If we do not learn from the experience we will not be generalizing from the experience; we will be generalizing the emotion, the thought, or idea that is holding that experience in place. Consequently, we will not be able to go past the experience itself. We will be fixated at that point and it will be affecting our choices, our relationships, and eventually our body.

What occurs in generalization is that we will have an experience. The experience will be affecting our thoughts, our emotions, and our choices. The problem with it is that it is not just the specific experience that is going to be the obstacle. We are going to generalize from that experience to any experience which is *similar* to it. Consequently, we will be operating *as if* an experience that has some aspects of similarity is exactly the same as the original. Instead of taking the time to see what other possibilities are available we will assume, on the unconscious level, that the experience is the same as another one that had a particular outcome. Further, since there are *some* similarities, this experience will have the same outcome. Actually the outcome does become pretty much the same because we make the same choices as we did before even though there is a high possibility that the choices do not work.

One reason that people have problems is because they are making choices that are not working. They are making choices based on the generalizations of the choices from the experiences that they have had, not based on the experience that they are having now.

This is important to understand about energy because the energy of the emotion, the thought, and idea that we are holding on to is going to be affecting the different parts of our body and eventually our whole body. In *Psychokinesiology* we will be working with the organs and with the energies associated with those organs.

The Chinese were probably the first to actually understand that our physical energies affect the organs of our bodies. You are most likely familiar with the ideas of acupuncture and acupressure and the concept that there is an energy that flows through the body which the Chinese call Ch'i (Qi), the Japanese call Ki, and in India it is called Prana. This is all the same energy and it is the life-force that keeps us alive and functioning. Some researchers have found that there is this energy that actually does flow and have been able to measure it. Before acupuncture began receiving acceptance in the United States it was accepted in Europe and was studied. The German physiologists and researchers were able to map 400 new points beyond the 600 that the Chinese had already mapped. Researchers have found that there is an energy flow that goes through the body which peaks at the acupuncture points. In fact, Dr. Robert O. Becker in his book, **The Body Electric** describes his research measuring the acupuncture points. What he corresponded the acupuncture points to were the transformers on electrical utility poles which boost the electrical current and send it on.

The Ch'i is related to particular meridians of the body and the meridians are related to specific organs in the body. Each of the organs of the body have a unique relationship to certain emotions and emotional responses. As we look at individual emotions we can see that there are *Primary Level Emotions, Secondary Level Emotions*, and *Base Level Emotions*. In the Base Level Emotions are both Positive and Negative Emotions. In Pk, what we do is to test the organs to find if it is in a particular organ where the energy is being held in place which is related to the problem state. *Psychokinesiology* does not use exactly the same points as acupuncture because there are 600 main points and 400 secondary points so finding the most advantageous point for the particular organ is a matter of conjecture. There are though, specific points that we will be using that are associated with the different organs and some of these points may be loosely associated with the acupuncture points while others are associated with certain areas and muscle groups in the body. Consequently, the energy can be easily tested by either touching the point or directing the hand at the point itself and muscle testing.

Then, with the Primary, Secondary, and Base emotions you can find the specific emotion that is related to the idea or experience. For example, you have done your basic questioning and you have found out that the problem is one of procrastination. When you go down through the *Emotional Reflex Points* you will find that the arm goes weak at one of the points. By checking the emotional responses you can find which specific emotion underlies the procrastination. After you have found the specific emotion then you can do a *Time Reversal* and find out if there was an original time for the emotion and the procrastination and do your *Resource Realigning* on it and clear it out of the way.

The use of the organs for testing is much more efficient and effective than consistently using *Retrograde Polarities*. The *Retrograde Polarities* are very good to find out the conflict that your client is having and testing after the *Resource Realigning*. Sometimes all that you need to do is to find the *Retrograde Polarity* and do a *Resource Realigning* on it and it clears it away helping your client to accomplish a lot more. In fact, what may happen is that you may clear away a number of things and there may still be an underlying *Retrograde Polarity* that needs your attention. Once that is taken care of then the Generative Change which occurs from a Pk session is put into action.

When doing the testing on the organs, one of the things that you need to remember is that whenever you get a weak response this indicates an energy imbalance going into and coming out of the organ. This is not the same as a "yes" or "no" response or as the weak/strong response in the *Time Reversal Procedure*. If there is an energy imbalance that is going into the organ this indicates that there is an energy imbalance someplace else. If there is an energy imbalance coming out of the organ it is going to affect other organs. Our whole body is a system which works as a unit and when the whole system is functioning properly it is working at its optimum. Unfortunately, that does not always happen. We will end up holding on to thoughts, ideas, and emotions instead of releasing them and allowing ourself to experience what is actually happening in our environment. Whenever we hold on to these thoughts, ideas, and emotions we are affecting our whole system and are changing the system so that it is not operating properly and efficiently.

It is interesting whenever you test an organ and have your client think of the problem state, you come up with an emotion. Quite often the emotion that you relate to the client makes sense to him and he can understand how it connects together. One of the most fascinating things about Pk is that when the person does make the connection it is not a connection where there is going to be much of a catharsis or other emotional expression. Your client will understand it from a different perspective looking at it differently almost immediately. In many instances, this is enough to cause change. One of the more fascinating aspects of *Psychokinesiology* is that change is almost immediate. Some people experience change as they are on the table. Others find change occurring quickly in their lives.

Another thing to remember about the use of muscle testing is that you are not testing muscle strength. You are actually testing the energy that is associated with the thought, idea, or emotion as well as the energy held up in the organ whenever your client is thinking of the problem state. Whenever you are testing a certain muscle or organ and the energy flow is disrupted the energy level is going to fall and the associated muscle test is going to be weak. If it is not disrupted at all you will have a strong response.

Following are the locations of the Organs and their Primary, Secondary, and Base Level Emotions associated with them. The listing will be by the Organ and its location, its Primary Level Emotion(s), its Secondary Level Emotions, and its Base Level Emotions both Positive and Negative Emotions. There are several ways to use the Organ/Emotion Chart: 1) simply ask; "Which organ is associated with this problem state?" and go down testing the Organs one by one; 2) have your client think of the problem state and touch each reflex point and test; 3) have your client think of the problem state and run your hand over each of the organs listed on the chart and test; or 4) if you know the emotion test the Organ as your client thinks about the problem state.

Once you have found the organ associated with the problem state ask: "Yes or no, Is the associated emotion the Primary Emotion? Hold." If not, then ask: "Yes or no, Is it the Secondary emotion? Test." If it is not the Secondary go the the Positive and Negative Emotions asking: "Yes or no, is the associated emotion a Negative Emotion? Hold." Once you have gotten to the Base Level Emotions and you know if it is a Positive or Negative emotion then ask and test: "Yes or no, Is the associated emotion from 1 to 5?" "Yes or no, 6 to 10?" You can then narrow the emotion down to the specific emotion(s). You can get more than one emotion associated with the problem state.

Once the emotion(s) are narrowed down then ask your client: "In reference to (<u>problem state</u>) does (<u>emotion</u>) make sense?" In the vast majority of cases the emotion(s) that you have found *will* make sense to your client. Probably the only times that they do not make sense is when the *Time of Origin* of the problem state is either in utero or is a genetic inheritance. There are also a few times when an association is not made because of conscious blocking of the association. Even if there is a conscious blocking a *Resource Realigning* will still be effective. Remember, you are not dealing with the conscious mind at all with *Psychokinesiology*.

We will begin at the top of the chart.

Organ	**Deep Emotions 2**
Location	On either side of forehead at the hairline **(Figure 8-5)**
Primary Emotions	**Impotent, frigid**
Secondary Emotions	Vain, lack of influence, hypertense, passionless
Base Emotions	**Negative Emotions**

Negative Emotions

1. Introverted	6. Conforming
2. Pompous	7. Defenseless
3. Compulsive	8. Unresponsive
4. Inflexible	9. Stressed-out
5. Sexless	10. Barren

Positive Emotions

1. Adaptable	6. Decorum
2. Obedient	7. Compliant
3. Good-Natured	8. Compromise
4. Conventional	9. Zealous
5. Life of the Party	10. Prolific

Figure 8-5

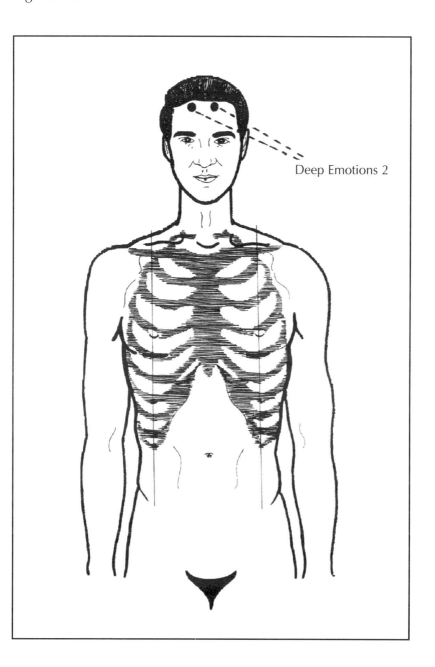

Deep Emotions 2

Figure 8-6

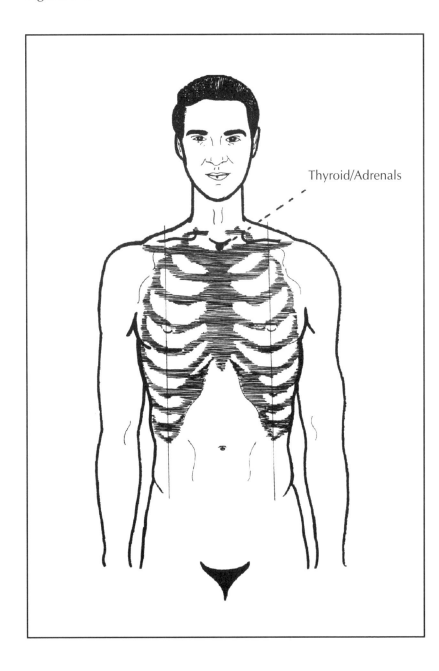

Organ	**Thyroid/Adrenals**
Location	(Thyroid) In the "V" notch in the center of the chest between the collar bones.
	(Adrenals) Four points: about 1" on each side of and about 1" above and below the navel. **(Figure 8-6)**
Primary Emotion	**Muddled instability**
Secondary Emotions	Confused thinking, paranoia, neurotic, mood swings, puzzled
Base Emotions	**Negative Emotions**

1. Dementia
2. Befuddled
3. Bipolar
4. Confusion
5. Contradictory
6. Argumentative
7. Demanding
8. Repulsive
9. Ridiculing
10. Overly Emotional

Positive Emotions
1. At Ease
2. Delighted
3. Exacting
4. Friendship
5. Cherish
6. Tolerant
7. Noble
8. Pleasant
9. Agreeable
10. Witt

Figure 8-7

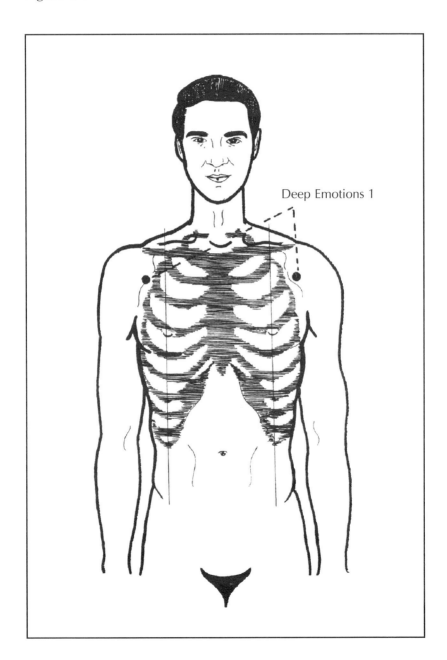

Organ	**Deep Emotions 1**
Location	About 2" directly above the crease of both armpits. **(Figure 8-7)**
Primary Emotions	**Worthlessness, Unworthy, Useless**
Secondary Emotions	Shameful, uncaring, vague, superficial, vengeful
Base Emotions	**Negative Emotions**

1. Unproductive
2. Conceit
3. Ineffective
4. Boring
5. Wasteful
6. Unkempt
7. Wreckless
8. Unimaginative
9. Humorless
10. Futile

Positive Emotions

1. Systematic
2. Logical
3. Methodical
4. Disciplined
5. Orderly
6. Organized
7. Busy
8. Indulgent
9. Friendly
10. Composed

Figure 8-8

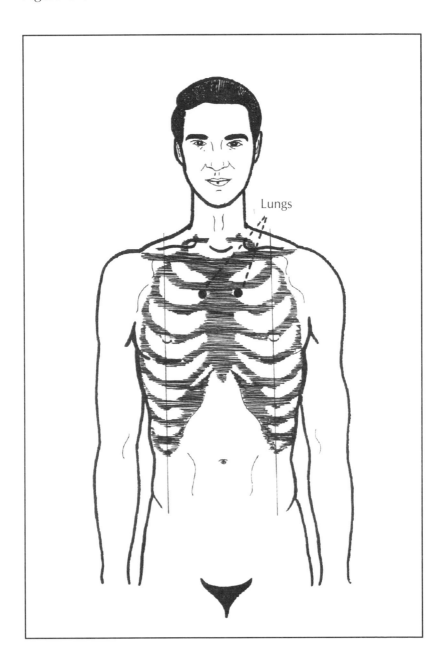

Organ	**Lungs**
Location	Two points: on either side of the sternum about 3" below the lower portion of the collar bone. **(Figure 8-8)**
Primary Emotion	**Grief**
Secondary Emotions	Dejected, pining, foggy thinking, torment, sadness
Base Emotions	**Negative Emotions**

Negative Emotions

1. Melancholy
2. Self-Pity
3. Perplexed
4. Heartache
5. False pride
6. Haughty
7. Depressed
8. Scorn/Disdain
9. Intolerance
10. Regret

Positive Emotions

1. Cheerful
2. Humility
3. Modesty
4. Openness
5. Tolerance
6. Optimistic
7. Unselfish
8. Meek
9. Accessible
10. Patient

Figure 8-9

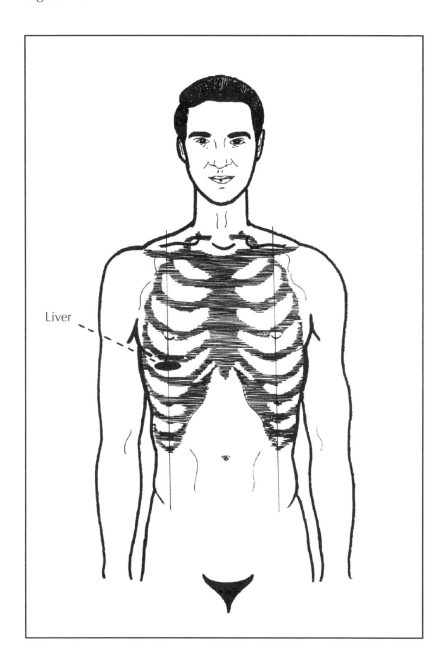

Organ	**Liver**
Location	Across and about 1" below the center line of the right chest. **(Figure 8-9)**
Primary Emotion	**Anger**
Secondary Emotions	Annoyed, agitated, irrationality, aggressive
Base Emotions	**Negative Emotions**

Negative Emotions

1. Unreasonable
2. Disappointed
3. Hostility
4. Shame
5. Persecuted
6. Jealous/Envy
7. Spiteful
8. Irritability
9. Abused
10. Resentment

Positive Emotions

1. Responsibility
2. Transformation
3. Happiness
4. Comfortable
5. Conscientious
6. Reliable
7. Firm
8. Careful
9. Gratitude
10. Pleased

Figure 8-10

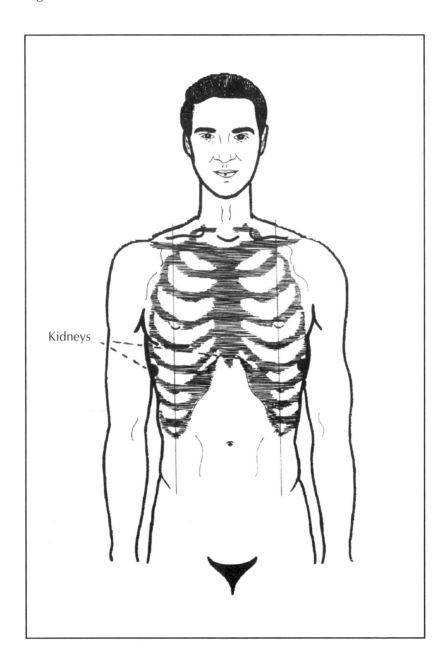

Organ	**Kidneys**
Location	Two locations: on either side of the chest about 4" below the armpit. **(Figure 8-10)**
Primary Emotion	**Fear**
Secondary Emotions	Dread, absent mindedness, thinking too much
Base Emotions	**Negative Emotions**

1. Foreboding
2. Forgetfulness
3. Phobia
4. Superstitious
5. Disloyal
6. Neglectful
7. Reckless
8. Inconsistent
9. Overcautious
10. Sexual Insecurity

Positive Emotions

1. Contemplative
2. Decisive
3. Loyal
4. Cautious
5. Sexual Security
6. Stability
7. Inventive
8. Resolute
9. Trusting
10. Satisfaction

Figure 8-11

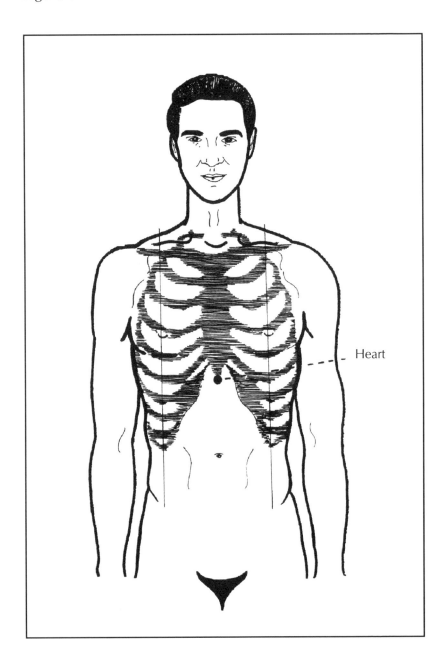

Organ	**Heart**
Location	At the bottom tip of the sternum. **(Figure 8-11)**
Primary Emotion	**Frightfully Excited**
Secondary Emotions	Out-of-place laughter, overly talkative, emotionally unresponsive, rapid speech and gestures
Base Emotions	**Negative Emotions**

1. Emotionlessness
2. Gabby
3. Manic Actions
4. Hate
5. Self-Doubt
6. Fickle
7. Distrust
8. Death
9. Bears Grudges
10. Abusive

Positive Emotions

1. Forgiveness
2. Compassion
3. Love
4. Secure
5. Thoughtfulness
6. Self-Worth
7. Generosity
8. Ecstatic
9. Sex
10. Benevolent

Figure 8-12

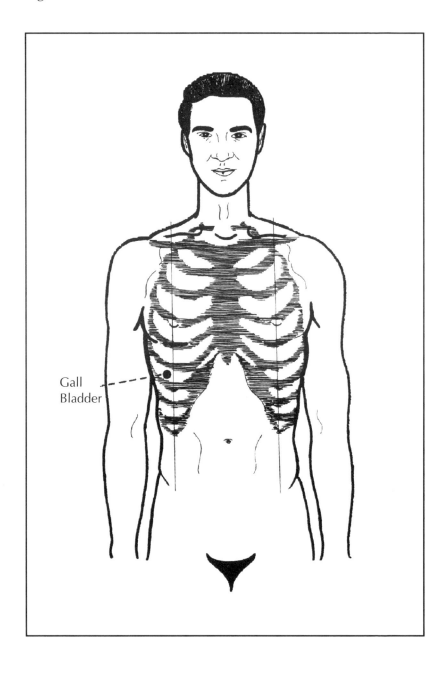

Gall
Bladder

Organ	**Gall Bladder**
Location	On the right side of the body to the right of the center line of the chest and about 3" down. **(Figure 8-12)**
Primary Emotion	**Resentment**
Secondary Emotions	Simmering anger, resistant, emotionally bound, indecisive, procrastination
Base Emotions	**Negative Emotions**

1. Impudence
2. Stubborn
3. Sullenness
4. Rage/Wrath
5. Self-Righteous
6. Boredom
7. Passive
8. Helpless
9. Inadequate
10. Arrogance

Positive Emotions

1. Choice
2. Adoration
3. Motivated
4. Options
5. Proud
6. Forgiving
7. Assertive
8. Jovial
9. Devotion
10. Honest

Figure 8-13

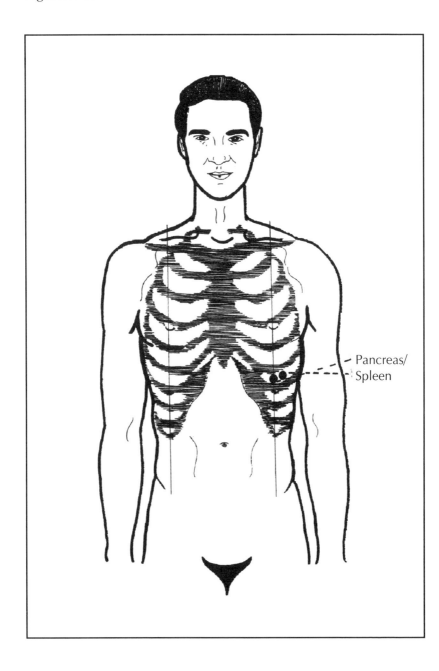

Organ	**Pancreas/Spleen**
Location	(Pancreas) On the left side of the chest about 2" directly below the nipple.
	(Spleen) On the left side of the chest about 1" to the left of the center line about 2" below the nipple. **(Figure 8-13)**
Primary Emotion	**Low Self-Esteem**
Secondary Emotions	Vicarious living, over-concern, hopelessness, lack of control, troubled, misgivings
Base Emotions	**Negative Emotions**

1. Self-Delusion
2. Overly-Anxious
3. Desperation
4. Suspicion
5. Distress
6. Surrender
7. Submissive
8. Deserted
9. Lack of Love
10. Destructive

Positive Emotions

1. Consideration
2. Confidence
3. Faith in the Future
4. Assurance
5. Dedicated
6. Gracious
7. Steadfast
8. Fulfillment
9. Elation
10. Bliss

Figure 8-14

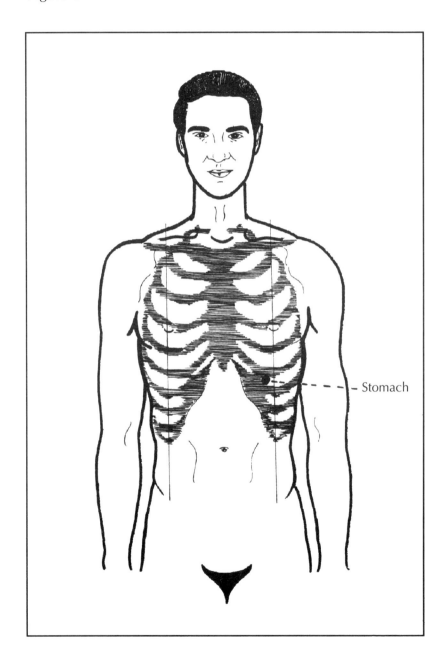

Organ	**Stomach**
Location	On the left side about 1" to the right of the center line of the chest about 2" below the nipple. **(Figure 8-14)**
Primary Emotion	**Over-Sensitivity**
Secondary Emotions	Self-aggrandizement, fixated, egoistic, quit, anxious, disgust, inhibited
Base Emotions	**Negative Emotions**

Negative Emotions

1. Loathing
2. Self-Obsessed
3. Dejection
4. Tense
5. Restrained
6. Disappointment
7. Greed
8. Criticism
9. Doubt
10. Bitterness

Positive Emotions

1. Compatibility
2. Empathy
3. Harmony
4. Reliable
5. Contentment
6. Sincerity
7. Accepting
8. Enthusiastic
9. Faithfulness
10. Expectancy

Figure 8-15

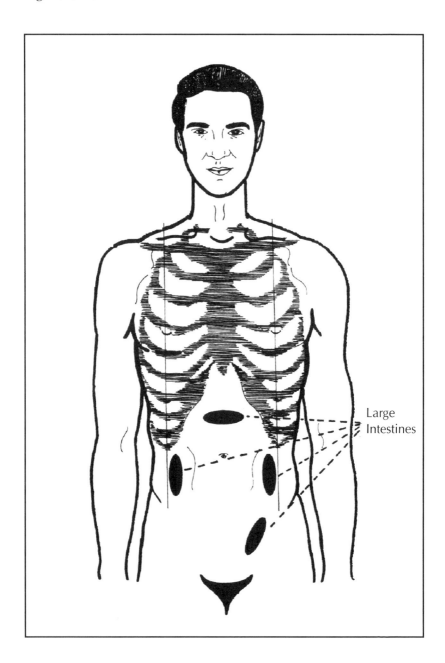

Organ	**Large Intestines**
Location	Four locations: In the center line of the body about 3" below the lower tip of the sternum; on the left side of the body about 1" below and to the right of the lower point of the chest; on the right side of the body about 1" below and to the left of the lower point of the chest; and on the left side of the body about 2" below the left side location on a downward diagonal on the pelvic girdle. **(Figure 8-15)**
Primary Emotions	**Coerced, Forced, Feeling Controlled**
Secondary Emotions	Weeping, obsessively neat, temperamental
Base Emotions	**Negative Emotions**

Negative Emotions

1. Mourning
2. Fastidious
3. On Edge
4. Obstinate
5. Judgmental
6. Compulsive
7. Uncertainty
8. Selfish
9. Dominating
10. Unmerciful

Positive Emotions

1. Refinement
2. Creative
3. Imaginative
4. Affection
5. Faithful
6. Serenity
7. Compassion
8. Inspired
9. Peaceful
10. Joyful

Figure 8-16

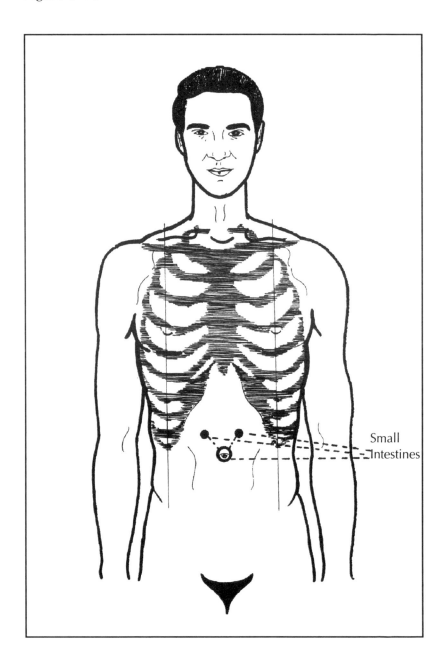

Organ	**Small Intestine**
Location	Three points: the navel, about 2" above and to the left of the navel, about 2" above and to the right of the navel. **(Figure 8-16)**
Primary Emotions	**Feeling lost, vulnerable**
Secondary Emotions	Abandoned, left alone, unloved, insecure, unfulfilled love
Base Emotions	**Negative Emotions**

Negative Emotions

1. Forsaken
2. Neglected
3. Unsure of self
4. Denied Love
5. Shock
6. Suppression
7. Discouraged
8. Unappreciated
9. Hurting
10. Forgetful

Positive Emotions

1. Assimilation
2. Nurturing
3. Pleased with Self
4. Overly Excited
5. Appreciated
6. Hopeful
7. Balance
8. Helpful
9. Solitude
10. Carefree

Figure 8-17

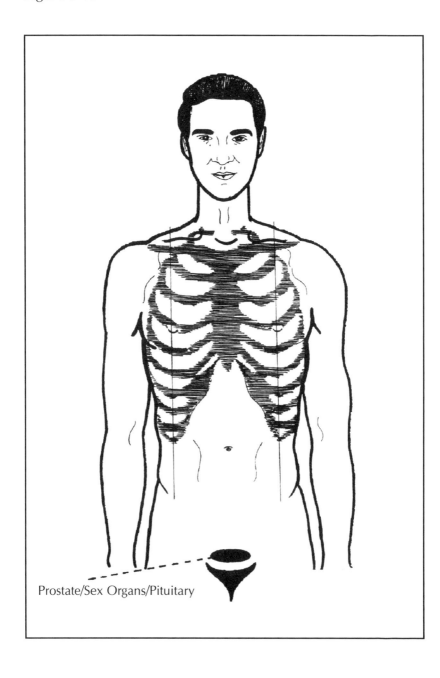

Prostate/Sex Organs/Pituitary

Organ	**Prostate/Sex Organs/Pituitary**
Location	(Prostate/Uterus) In the center line of the body 1" above the pubic bone.
	(Ovaries) On either side of the center line of the body about 3" above the pubic bone. (Testes) On the groin.
	(Pituitary) On the inside of each eye beside the nose. **(Figure 8-17)**
Primary Emotions	**Absence of thinking and feeling**
Secondary Emotions	Dissipated, emotionally restrained, lethargic, lucid dreaming, apathetic memory
Base Emotions	**Negative Emotions**

1. Devitalized
2. Repressed
3. Mental Inertia
4. Guilt
5. Apathy
6. Dishonest
7. Remorse
8. Rejection
9. Cynical
10. Immorality

Positive Emotions

1. Truthful
2. Warmth
3. Energetic
4. Passion
5. Intimacy
6. Dignity
7. Genius
8. Joyful
9. Extroversion
10. Fantasizing

Figure 8-18

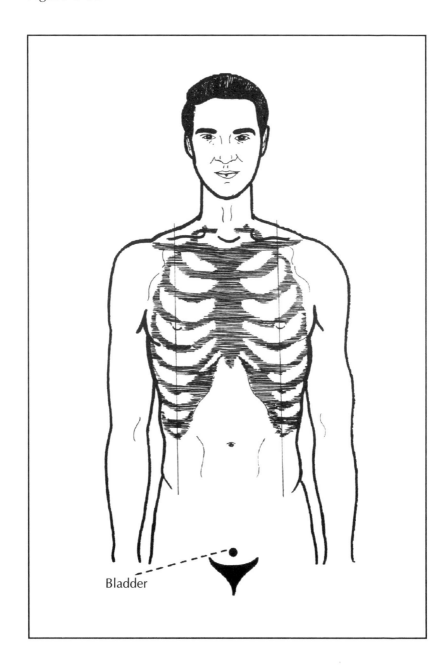

Bladder

Organ	**Bladder**
Location	In the center line of the body on the top of the pubic bone. **(Figure 8-18)**
Primary Emotion	**"Can't", frozen will power**
Secondary Emotions	Offended, shy, incompetent, vague, blasé attitude
Base Emotions	**Negative Emotions**

1. Insulted
2. Timid
3. Careless
4. Vacillating
5. Mediocrity
6. Fearful
7. Terror
8. Restlessness
9. Frustration
10. Powerlessness

Positive Emotions

1. Adequacy
2. Inner Directed
3. Tranquility
4. Quietness
5. Calm
6. Composure
7. Perfectionism
8. Desire
9. Courage
10. Accurate

CHAPTER 9

RESOURCE REALIGNING

Discussion thus far has centered on accessing the problem state and finding the information needed in order to do a *Resource Realigning*. You have seen how to gain rapport, to do basic information gathering, to find out what needs to be changed, and basic calibration for muscle testing. You know how to test to make sure that your client is "wired" appropriately and to test the problem state. You have seen the technique to inquire if you have the information necessary to do the *Resource Realigning*. You have the technique for doing a *Time Reversal* and have the *Emotional Reflex Points* associated with the organs. Now, you will learn several techniques for realigning your client's resources. Before discussing the techniques, there are some aspects of the mind that need to be understood

Whenever you were born, you were born whole and with all of your resources in place. The resources became misaligned through your experience with your environment. As you were growing up you were taught by significant others how to deal with your environment. Reward and punishment created specific behaviors, values, attitudes, and belief structures. These behaviors, values, and so forth worked for the people who taught them to you but you are not them. Taking on these behaviors, values, and so on misaligned many of your resources. Others got misaligned as other persons and experiences influenced you. To get an understanding of how the resources work it is necessary to have an understanding of how your mind is structured. Remember that your mind affects your body, your experiences, and your body and your experiences affect your mind in a constant feedback loop. When things happen to you physically on your body or experientially in your life it is because of this feedback loop and the interplay of the resources.

To begin with, the mind is what the brain does. What this means is that according to researchers today the mind is defined as a series of *processes* occurring in the brain. It is not a thing like the brain that can be measured. The mind is essentially the subjective experience of the brain and can be divided into two parts. One part is aware of things going on outside of you as well as internal feelings and sensations. This is the conscious part of the mind. It works to keep what you see, hear, feel, taste, and smell consistent and without separation. It makes sure that all of your present experiences are within the parameters of your past experiences and the beliefs you hold about these experiences. In other words, its awareness of your experience must follow a set pattern of interpretation. This pattern is *cause and effect*.

The conscious part of your mind is made up of whatever you are aware of at the present time both internally and externally as well as your ego identifications and everything to which you attach a meaning. Your identity is part of your consciousness. It is composed of everything that you see, hear, feel, taste, and smell as well as your memories and thoughts and the feelings attached to them at any particular point in time. Your ego identity is sort of a gatekeeper for your conscious mind. If your ego does not perceive of something it does not come into your awareness. Hence, it is a filter for your experience insuring a consistency to your experience.

There is a unique interdependence between the brain and the conscious self. The feelings of love, hate, joy, fear, or values such as truth, goodness, and beauty apply to mental appraisals and are experienced. Whatever the brain has come to accept fully will be experienced by the conscious self. We will love only those things and people with which we have been *conditioned* to love, hate those things which we have been *conditioned* to hate, be afraid of those things which we have been *conditioned* to fear, and accept the values with which we have learned and with which we are most familiar. We cannot do otherwise.

The other part of the mind is aware of what is going on deeply inside of you. It keeps track of all of those experiences that you have forgotten and from time to time expresses itself with emotions, feelings, ideas, and thoughts that have nothing to do with what is going on outside of you.

This is because it has no sense of space and time. It is the unconscious mind. It can experience what is happening on the outside taking all of this information and seeing it from a different perspective. Since it keeps track of those forgotten previous experiences it has a wider range of events to deal with and to work from. It associates experiences together that the conscious mind would not and comes to its own conclusions. The two main aspects of the unconscious: that it has no sense of time or space, and that it takes *all* experience into account contribute to its design.

The unconscious is sort of a receptacle that holds together all of the mental activities that do not harmonize with your awareness of yourself or your consciousness. There are the forgotten experiences and memories and experiences that are too weak for the conscious mind to deal with. Things that do not stay long in consciousness are repressed and are placed into the unconscious. The conscious mind may use some of the unconscious information from time to time but this tends to be to a limited degree. One of the most important aspects of the unconscious is that it contains *complexes*. Complexes are thoughts, ideas, and beliefs that have behavioral patterns, emotions, and *resource states* attached to and surrounding them. Complexes are major influences in your behavior. Anyone that tends to behave in habitual ways is acting upon a complex. Rather, they are using the resources that have become attached to that complex.

We tend to think that our personality is a singular thing. This it is not. Our personality is constructed of all of our experiences, learnings, thoughts, and so forth up to the present time. As the Gestalt psychologists have said, "The whole is different than the sum of its parts," so is our total personality different than the sum of our experiences. It is an interaction of all of the parts as well as all of the resources associated with all of the parts that make up who we are.

Brain researchers do not speak of parts but of *processors* in the brain. Essentially the mind is made up of a large number of these processors. Each of them is connected to other processors and between resources and they keep lists of what things are useful and in what situations. Each of the processors has specific goals that they single-mindedly pursue. They learn which resources they can borrow and what signals to send to other processors in order to get their jobs done.

Everything in the mind is decentralized. This is necessary because of the many little processes which are needed for the performance of a skill. One processor is dependent upon another because each one has learned how to exploit other processors so that all of the processors maximize each other and their available potential. This insures that every one of them will get the complete benefit of the total experience and data of the other.

All knowledge in the mind manifests itself in the connections made in the brain. This is a result of the natural growth of the dendrites of the neurons during exploration and learning episodes. The mind's knowledge is dispersed in an intricate web of interacting connections. It is not the processors themselves but how they are linked that captures the essence of an experience. Ideas are linked through learned associations and their accompanying neural images which are left after an experience. It is through these images that our associations are made. Each of the processors of the mind function to report part of the story of the experience. It is through the conglomeration of stories where we get the entire story. Through the complete image of an experience we make other associations and are able to relate and generalize concerning any situation. This is how we are able to relate to and learn from the experience.

Thinking is an internalized process which deals with symbols and the manipulation of concepts and precepts. It is a *representational* mental process. It consists of a train of ideas and a problem solving activity involving mainly creative operations. It comes in many forms, some of which include abstract thinking, associative thinking, autistic thinking, primary process thinking, concrete thinking, and magical thinking. All of these processes of thinking are indicative of particular states of consciousness. These in turn indicate an individual's belief systems. It is through your beliefs that you experience your world.[1]

The beliefs which you hold are essentially a set of categorizations and values that are brought into your interactions. They are formed from your earliest learning experiences. These learning experiences include familial behavioral patterns which you have picked up, attitudes and traits which you have encountered outside of the family and have

---

[1] In order for something to be true by nature, it must be inherent in the organism. Since literally *all* philosophies, concepts, beliefs, and dogma are made up, they are *not* true naturally.

accepted, conditioning and training procedures which have instructed you in specific behaviors, acceptance of things which you have been told, and other things which you have just picked up throughout your wanderings. *No* beliefs are innate to the human being, or any other animal for that matter. You are *not* born believing anything. You have to be *taught* what to believe.

Your belief system consists of a series of *Belief Networks* or *models of the way you draw causal inferences about the world.* They can become very complicated in keeping with the fact that your world, and your understanding of it, can be very complicated. This complexity is due to the fact that any given event can be the result of any number of possible causes thus producing any number of effects. No matter how complex a given belief network is, the process of reasoning with those beliefs will still be governed by the same principles.

Whatever your belief system, causality—cause/effect relationships—is its base. These relationships are due to associations made between events which appear to or actually do follow preceding phenomena.

Causality can simply be stated in this way: Every event has some sort of preceding cause or causes. You must understand that all events in the world cannot possibly influence all other events. What you are doing at this time and in this space reading these words has virtually no influence over something occurring in some jungle tribe in Borneo or some modern city in Europe. It also has no influence over someone who is reading about belief systems in another part of the country, or even in another part of your house. A given event has only a limited number of possible causes. This expresses the concept of *Limited* or *Finite Causality.*

There are several issues in cause/effect relationships. First of all, we must deal with the notion of *Temporal Contiguity: events occurring in time.* Seeing things transpiring at the same time can easily lead you to think that the two events are related. In the majority of instances this is not the case. A series of events which appear to stand out due to the time sequence in which they are occurring do not necessarily have anything to do with each other. Superstitions and superstitious behaviors and religious beliefs begin this way. As an example: Someone is walking down a street. Across the sidewalk a ladder is stretched in order for a workman to do some work. Since there is no other place to walk the person is compelled to walk under the ladder. A few blocks down the street this person is mugged and robbed. Upon getting up from the sidewalk walking under the ladder was remembered and an association was drawn between walking under the ladder and the mugging. There is no thought that the person may have been in an area of town which is not very safe and in which there are frequent muggings. As you can see, temporal contiguity is an insufficient basis from which to draw conclusions.

The next notion that we must deal with is that of *Spatial Contiguity*, or *events occurring in the same space*. Events which seem to occur in the same space do not necessarily occur at the same time. If there are two automobile accidents at the same place several days apart it does not mean they were both caused by the *same* preceding events. Also, we cannot conclude that two or more events occurring in the same place at the same time (temporally and spatially contiguous) are caused by the same preceding events. There are some events which are spatially contiguous but are non-existent such as illusions or hallucinations.[2] Others can be both spatially and temporally contiguous and have nothing to do with each other. The concept of limited causality leads us to the *Principle of Determinism: every natural event has a cause, and looking hard enough, we can find that cause.*

Temporality is a function of the conscious mind. There are *no* events for which we cannot find a cause on the physical level. Those we cannot explain at this point in time and space are not "mysteries." We simply do not have the appropriate equipment (whether it be mechanical, electrical, mental, or any other sort) to explain them. By simply assuming that it is a mystery or is caused by some event which cannot be proven is tantamount to giving up. The human brain is constructed for learning and experience. It is built in such a way that the greater the amount of learning, the more connections it makes and the more efficient it becomes. The more efficient it is the more it can learn and the more effective it becomes in relation to adjusting and experiencing its external environment.

---

2   Hallucinations are spatially contiguous for the person who is experiencing the hallucinations, not for any one else. Just because someone is experiencing the hallucination does not mean that it actually exists in space and time. The experience is only within the subjective reality of the hallucinator.

Causes and consequences can be codified into a few straight-forward rules of inference. One of the main methods of this codification is by way of *Analogy*. Analogy is *making comparisons or drawing parallels*. It is simply reasoned as: *the same as; different than;* or *similar to*. Human performance in this area is governed by two different set of rules: one concerns itself with access to analogies and the other with inference from analogies. Analogy is a powerful tool in human thought. We reason and learn by analogy and our language is filled with analogy in the form of metaphors and idiomatic expressions. Language itself is an analogy. Words only *represent* the objects and events which they depict and are not the object or event. Whenever we generalize an experience that we have had to another experience or to other experiences we are creating an analogy. Analogy is seen in our social, governmental, educational, and especially religious institutions as well as the social structure and society at large. We represent our countries, our religions, our self by analogy and metaphor. Hence, analogy and metaphor may be considered the basis for human society.

When humans think, there are some typical patterns which they follow. When confronted with a new situation, we will often recall a similar situation in the past and reason by analogy to apply the experience of it to the present situation. In other words, we generalize that the two events are similar and may have the same or similar outcomes. In essence, we are assuming that they have the same or similar preceding causes.

Although analogy is obviously a very important tool in human thought, it is very tricky and dangerous for it can easily be misunderstood. It is easy to mistake the "map" for the "territory" as it were. We tend to do this with the language that we speak and the experiences that we encounter. We assume that what is being said is what we understand, or that the experience we are having is close enough to one (or more) which we have previously encountered that it will lead to the same outcome.

The most solid analogies tend to be those which take into account the causal and structural parallels between situations, as opposed to superficial details. This is the *Structure Mapping Theory of Analogy*. In other words, this is *seeing the map as different from the territory*. What appears to be the same is only on the surface of the experience: the map. The territory is the actual causal relationship that exists in the event.

Most persons make assumptions from their own experience that there is a particular experience with which they have at one time dealt, which is the cause. Consequently, they will see the same results. They do not consider that there are other causes outside of their limited experience which are possible.

Finite causality does not mean that there is *only* one cause or a series of causes with which we are familiar which lead to a certain event. It means that there are any number of causes for the event with a myriad of them outside of your experience.

How we think has been the subject of much discussion for countless centuries. What goes on to produce thought has remained quite a mystery. . . until we have been able to get some understanding of the workings of the brain itself. It must be remembered that when we are born we have no thoughts nor do we think. All that we have is *experience and association*. It is this ability which files away experiences in our brain creating dendritic attachments from neuron to neuron. We have no real ability to think until we have a language. Without the use of language we cannot categorize the objects and events which we experience. Language is a *symbolic* way of representing our experience. With language we can communicate whatever we have encountered whether internally or externally. But since it is a symbol it can only *represent* what we are attempting to communicate and can never be the actual expression of that communication: The map is *not* the territory. This is where problems with communicating come to light. Symbols do not always represent the same things to everyone.

After we have had an experience of some sort there is a neural trace or image left in the brain. The idea of an image is most appropriate. For the majority of persons the vast preponderance of our experience is visual and comes to us in visual form thus remaining an image in the brain. Hence, the term neural image suits the process best. Further, the current view of the function of our memory employs images. Look, also, at the popular memory training courses, they make an extensive use of visual imagery in order to increase mental abilities. It has also been postulated that prior to every movement we make it is seen as an image in the brain. Remember also that every neuron is somehow involved either directly or peripherally in every experience that we have and in everything that we do. Consequently, with this in mind, each neuron has a picture or image of the total performance of your brain and its experience.

It is a fact that every neuron on one side of the brain has a mirror image on the other side. Due to this, there is a good potential that even with impairment we can still relearn a skill. When it comes to relearning the skill there is less time involved because the learning sequence is still intact in each neuron.

The same goes for each thought you think. A thought is self-stimulation of input, processing, and output. A thought is an experience, but it is a contained experience within the whole brain itself. Each thought would then, since it is an experience, be contained within each neuron the same as a physical experience. As researchers have found, the brain is not able to tell the difference between a physical or imagined event. They are both the same.

The brain can be seen as embracing a total representation of your entire experience. That experience is contained within the brain in a three-dimensional hologram. The implications of this concept are far reaching. What this says is that each neuron contains its own consciousness. Besides that, each neuron has a representative consciousness of the *whole* individual. When it comes to defining and choosing your reality, it's all of these neuronal consciousnesses, the complete hologram, acting together which performs this function.

Even with consciousness being defined as simply a state of awareness, then you can see consciousness is not a uncomplicated process. It involves the whole brain and the 100 billion or so neurons of which the brain is comprised. Also, with each neuron having its own consciousness and being part of the greater consciousness of the brain, the form which is chosen for your reality is only part of the total available reality. What is chosen as the experience of reality depends upon the interaction of *nature* and *nurture*. The experience of the reality is mainly from nature; choices of the precise experiences within that experience of reality are learned.

The theory of the holographic brain was first developed by Emmett Leith and Juris Upatnieks by expanding on Dennis Gabor's holograms. You will recall that a hologram is a three-dimensional image on a surface such as glass. Holograms are a phenomenon of light waves. Like sound, light does not travel in straight lines. Light is *"warped."* "Warps" in the light relay to the eye the specific image which is in transit. The essence of all holograms is that they possess phase and it is these phase differences we see. These phase differences are a matter of angles.

Holographic plates distort incoming waves of light. These distortions appear as a moving three-dimensional image to the brain. Every piece of the hologram can by itself perform the same function as the total hologram. A portrait on glass, for example, when broken will be broken into pieces. Not so for a hologram. If a hologram is broken every piece of that broken hologram will contain an *exact* representation of the complete hologram. All of the pieces will not be in as much detail but they will all have the same image. Consequently, if you could examine a minute piece of the broken hologram you will see the same image in that piece as was in the original but without the detail.

The human brain works much the same way. Whenever we have an experience of any sort it will be stored in the brain in a precise three-dimensional, holographic model. Every experience, thought, or sensation is likewise accommodated and held in the brain in a complete three-dimensional holographic representation. Not only is this in the brain as a holographic image but, just like the man-made hologram, each neuron likewise has this very same holographic image. This occurs because each neuron is either directly or peripherally involved in every experience we have and in all we think and do. Just as with the broken hologram, it is not in as sharp an image as the whole brain but it is an exact three-dimensional copy. It is, then, all of these smaller copies which make up the whole image that we experience and remember. Thus, the whole *is* different than the sum of its parts.

Since every neuron is involved in your experience, and since every neuron has a complete picture of the experience of the whole brain then whatever you learn is imprinted not only on the particular neural network, but also on each and every neuron in the brain. For example, if you learn a bad habit, breaking that habit can become somewhat of an ordeal. There not only has to be a change in the particular neural network which directs the habitual stimulus to the brain but also all of the other neurons—being that they have some sort of involvement—must be recalibrated. If you have ever tried to break a habit of any sort, you know how difficult that can be. In essence, you have to *rethink* almost your whole life to get out of it. You need to cause an effect in each and every neuron of the brain due to its involvement in the first learning experience.

From the time we begin perceiving our own personal universe, information is being filed away in the recesses of our brain. The majority of this information is in the form of images. When we begin to understand that those noises proceeding from the mouths of the significant others have meaning, we begin associating those word/symbols to perceived objects and events. At that point experience is set aside and conscious thought begins to take over. This is when our consciousness commences a separation from ourself: of the "I" from the "non-I." We begin to isolate ourself from our creation, our personal universe, and begin to think of ourself as "different" and apart from everything else. We see ourself as a separate entity from the rest of physical creation. Once we see ourself as separate and apart we begin to have problems. We take on feelings of alienation, insecurity, and aloofness. We will place ourself in a position apart from others and see ourself as an object instead of a person. Once that occurs then we feel that it is perfectly fine to obliterate whatever is outside of ourself for we do not experience ourselves as authentic.

The basic structure of our universe is determined by how we *choose* to look at it. This includes not only the objects in our immediate environment but also our relationships. How we choose to look at our environment and our relationships are both determined by several factors. First, there is early conditioning set up by our significant others. Basic family patterns of action, belief, attitude, values, etc. are conditioned and thrust upon us without our knowledge or consent. This early conditioning, this early programming, sets the stage for much of our later development and choices.

Second, our choice of how we view our environment is determined not only by our early relationships with significant others but later with our peers. Our later relationships stem from our primary relationships. We will model many behaviors of those whom we have come to admire, especially significant others in or outside the immediate family. Modeling those behaviors has the side effect of modeling the person's state of consciousness and environmental viewpoint.

Third, we tend to see our environment through our self-concept, self-esteem, and self-image. Whatever view we have of ourself is the view we tend to *project* outward to our environment. If we see ourself as limited and controlled, our view of our environment will likewise be limited and controlled. If we see certain problems everywhere it is because we have those problems within ourselves. A low self-image, low self-esteem, and poor self-concept will be reflected in the way that we act, or react, in our environment.

Fourth, we tend to look at our environment based upon the present environmental situation. If we are in an unfamiliar situation how we choose to look at our environment determines how we will react within it. If the environment has limited light availability, sound reproduction, or some other sensory modifier, it will affect how we are going to perceive the situations we encounter within that environment.

Fifth, we will choose to look at our environment through the modifications placed on our basic personality. We are born with a series of functional behaviors which are designed to assist us in dealing with the outside world. As we grow and mature, we will begin to modify our behavior in order to fit into the patterns necessary for our survival. These patterns are imposed upon us by our society and its institutions, and will place limitations on our ability to express ourself and the choices we make in our environment.

Sixth, how we choose to look at our environment and the relationships that we have is also determined by our perspective on actuality. If we have the idea that what we are calling the world is not real, that it is an illusion and the "real" world is somewhere else or that it is attainable only after death, we will treat our experience as illusory and the people in it will be illusions. We will act in a way that is antisocial and possibly destructive and harmful to ourself and/or to others. Further, if we see this actuality as one that is manipulated by something outside of us we will act accordingly and use it to exploit others.

Seventh, we choose to look at our environment through our physiological make-up. We can perceive it no other way. If there is some distortion in our physical senses then we will view a distorted environment. Likewise, being colorblind shows us an environment which is different from the way others see it.

Last, we choose to look at our environment through our consciousness. What we are conscious of we will experience. Our consciousness, you see, is determined by all of the above processes. Simply put, we view our environment and our relationships through the consciousness we have for that particular environment and relationship.

What we perceive is nothing more than the creations of our mind. In essence, all we experience as physical reality or actuality is nothing more than external representations of internal realities and concepts. Our external experience is only a construction of our internal beliefs and conscious and unconscious motivations.

The brain is only a receiver, analyzer, reactor unit. It is the mind which does the creating. (Remember, the mind is a series of processes). The brain perceives. The mind interprets. The brain reacts. The mind creates. The brain analyzes. The mind processes.

The brain and the mind are often spoken of together but both of them are separate and distinct. They are seen in *coherent superposition* with each other. The brain is a physical entity. The mind is not. We can be relatively certain there is a connection between the brain, the mind, and consciousness. There is also a connection with your physical and mental well being. Many of the processes known as the mind control the physical processes within the brain. It is these physical processes in the brain which exert a command over the body. The mind does not *directly* affect the body.

The controller of our physical and mental well-being as well as our consciousness is thought. Thought is like the program to a computer and visual imagery is the computer language. We must remember when we were taught to speak we were taught that the words that we are learning represent physical objects. Words have a visual counterpart. Words can trigger visual images. It does not matter if we hear these words outside of our body or we say them to ourselves, the words we hear activate images in our brain. What we can then consider is the fact that if we hear or repeat something constantly over a long enough period of time, it will come to be accepted as factual by the brain and it will tend to be repeated as a physical behavior.

Consciousness is at the basis of *everything*. Without a certain level of awareness we could not perceive the reality that exists at that level. Thoughts tell us what our reality is, what to expect, and who we are. Thoughts also indicate our place in the scheme of things, and are the programs for our brain. Our *brains* process the information we are receiving and the *output* is our *perceived reality*.

Our thoughts exist in our mind as well as in time and space. They may, if pondered upon long enough, eventually manifest in the physical universe. It takes energy, both electrical and chemical, in order to think thoughts. Thoughts can then be seen as a form of energy. Thoughts, themselves, apparently do have a construction of some sort. Thoughts can attract to the thinker the original intent of the thought. This depends upon the strength of the thought. Simply stated, the more often you think a thought, the greater the chance of its realization.

We think on both conscious and unconscious levels. Both of these levels may not be in harmony all of the time. We can state consciously that something is necessary but unconsciously deny the need for it. An example is that of visual imagery in healing. Along with the visual imagery you need to have a positive attitude and a *desire* to have the healing in order for healing to be affected.

Conscious thoughts are more or less a mediator with the external environment. There is the possibility of them not even reflecting what is deep in our mind. Remember that we have both conscious *and* unconscious thinking processes. Our conscious thinking tends to be nothing more than a lot of repressed materials concerning mainly what we feel about ourselves, our environment, and what we desire out of life. In many instances, we do not have access to our inner thinking directly. We can get an understanding of much of our unconscious thinking by paying close attention to the unrealistic demands we are placing on ourselves and others. These will be reflected in many of the directions we choose and the relationships we have.

Resource Realigning is the way that you get your client's unconscious processes shifted to operate without conflict and congruently in reference to the problem state. The *Resource Realigning* process is actually a reintegration process. What you are actually doing whenever you are realigning your client's resources is reintegrating him so that he can operate more effectively and more efficiently in regards to the problem state. By realigning the resources you are shifting the internal processing of your client so that he will be able to have more opportunity to make changes, be more flexible and have more choices available.

Change can be rather disruptive to some people. Some people actually come away afraid of making change. Consequently, many people become comfortable in the behaviors, attitudes, and life-style that they have. It is easy to stay the same because the world is easier to deal with and more predictable. This "comfort zone" that they are living in is radiated from the deeper and more hidden thoughts that they have.

One of the more fascinating advantages of the *Resource Realigning* process is that your client will have actual change in many subtle ways; ways that they do not even realize at the time. The change is not one that is disruptive to them at all. You will often find that your client will be welcoming change. Many times after a *Resource Realigning*, your client will be expecting changes, and actually looking for things to happen. It is interesting that once a person gets into this frame of mind things do happen for them because *they are paying attention to it*. One of the problems with people is that they stay the same because they are not looking for change. Whenever you look for change you are going to find it. So, the *Resource Realigning* process reengages resources into a different pattern in the system. Once this occurs then different resources are brought into play changing your client's perspective and actions.

You will recall that consistent behaviors are generalized behaviors. What people do in order to support these behaviors is to set up filters that will shape their internal and external experience. If you find a way to reshape or readjust your perceptions you will find different ways of doing things. If you can create a powerful, intense peak experience it will harness your own creativity thus finding ways to learn from and control your experiences. The more flexibility and variability you have within, the more variability and response you will get in the output. What *Resource Realigning* does is increase the possibilities for greater flexibility and variability.

The property of a system where it uses the fewest number of distinctions to create the widest range of variability is known as *elegance*. Elegance is doing what you need to do in the fewest number of steps. It is a natural ongoing response process proceeding from one point of responding to another. True elegance brings everything into a cooperatively operating system. Each part of the system will be influencing other parts of the system in an orderly way. This causes a reorganization which rearranges the filters resulting in a change in the worldview. Since internal organization will be rearranged into different sequences experiences will have different meanings.

There are certain operational assumptions made about the *Resource Realigning* process:

1. The *Resource Realigning* process is one of *generative change*. This means that as change begins in one area of life it will generate into other areas. Since one of the major processes of the human brain is generalization once the way for change has been cleared in one area other associated areas will likewise begin to change. This is known because the *Psychokinesiology* process becomes quicker and easier with your client as time goes on.

2. People have all of the resources necessary in order to make the changes that they need to make. The problem behaviors stem from

having the resources attached in inappropriate ways. Once more appropriate resource attachments are made then change becomes easier.

3. Every behavior is an adaptive behavior. In essence, every behavior, even ones that are problems had a positive intent at the beginning. The chances are they even worked well at first. Unfortunately, they became a problem when they outlived their usefulness and continued on in spite of them being non-rewarding. The choices that they produced *were* worthwhile and the resources that they engaged *were* effective. All that needs to be done is to readjust the resources and the resulting behavior will be useful.

4. All external behavior is the result of internal processes. These internal processes are neurological and biochemical. This means that much of our motivating properties are *unconscious* and these unconscious motivators have a great deal of influence over our daily lives. The unconscious itself seems to be a behind-the-scenes director of our thinking and actions. It takes on habit patterns after they have been learned by the conscious mind. So, in order to have external change there needs to be an *internal* change. The *Resource Realigning* shifts these internal processes and makes them more accessible and amenable to change.

5. We are the creators of our experience. In order to make sense of our experience we create "mental maps" of each experience. These maps guide our choices and our behaviors. Since each one of us has our own map the experience that we have is totally unique to us. The *Resource Realigning* shifts and "updates" this map.

6. The *Resource Realigning* process increases individual self-worth. This is one of the immediate benefits of the process. This is the first generative change that occurs. Then as time goes on other aspects of life-style begin to subtly readjust and experiences that were troubling and frustrating before begin becoming easier to deal with and less frustrating.

7. A *Resource Realigning* creates a flexible system. The more flexible the system the more chance there is of adjusting to new experiences and readjusting to ones that got in the way. By shifting resources into a more accessible mode flexibility is created. This in turn alters consciousness in such a way that the problem state is viewed differently.

People are not "stuck." People *get* stuck. Most often their stuck state is the result of not paying attention to the choices available to them or opting not to make choices leading them to an "either/or" state. Once they get into that state they really have no choice at all. Getting out of that state involves reframing their view of the situation and reorganizing their resources thus producing the availability of greater choice and flexibility.

After you have all of the information necessary for *Resource Realigning* there are several methods that you can use to do this. One thing that you will notice is that one of the most important things in *Resource Realigning* is the breath. Increasing the flow of blood and oxygen to the brain will accomplish two things. First, it will activate areas of your brain that are usually idle from lack of blood. Second, it will slow the constant apoptosis (cellular death) of the brain cells.

Inside of your skull are the carotid arteries. They branch into smaller and more numerous arteries fanning out in an intricate lacy network of capillaries. This network of capillaries is designed to reach into every portion of your brain feeding as many neurons as possible. Even so, some will receive more blood than others and it is those which receive the least blood that are the first to die off. In order to arrest this process it is necessary to increase the blood flow into the brain. As more arterial blood flows into the brain an equal amount flows out through the veins washing away wastes and toxins that interfere with proper brain functioning.

The carotid arteries usually admit more blood than is needed in order to compensate for the increases in CO_2. An effective method for oxygenating the brain is to induce increases in CO_2 in the blood. Probably the most simple method for doing this is holding the breath several times and as long as possible over a period of several minutes. What the brain does is begin to deal with the automatic survival response. After several minutes when the brain is not getting the oxygen necessary it begins to pay attention to what is going on in its experience. If while you are holding your breath you are thinking about a problem behavior the brain will associate that problem behavior with survival. Since there will be an increased blood flow into the brain because of the increased CO_2, the association will be that this problem affects physical survival. Then, on the unconscious level, the brain will engage resources to overcome this problem. In order to engage the appropriate resources it is necessary to know the *precise* problem. That is what the basic information gathering process is all about.

Before you begin *Resource Realigning* it is wise to make sure that you have enough information to do the clearing. Have your client place her hand over her forehead palm down and ask: "Yes or no, do we have enough information to clear this now? Hold." You should get a strong (yes) response. The next step is to: Have your client close her eyes and ask, "Yes or no, do we do this clearing with the eyes closed? Hold." If you get a "yes" response have your client keep her eyes closed during the clearing process. If you are doing the clearing with the eyes closed make sure that you have your client focus her eyes into the center of her forehead all the while the realigning is going on. If you get a "no" response to the above question ask, "Yes or no, do we do this clearing with the eyes open? Hold." If you get a "yes" have your client keep her eyes open while the realigning is occurring. If you get a "yes" with both of them, it would be best to do the procedure with your client's eyes closed and test for both once completed.

The first *Resource Realigning* technique is this: Have your client lying on her back on the table. For about ten to fifteen seconds lightly rub her scalp over the four lobes of her brain with your fingers. **(Figure 9-1)** Then take your client's right arm with your left hand and muscle test with your right hand's thumb and forefinger spread across your client's forehead. **(Figure 9-2)** Have her take a deep breath and hold it thinking about the problem state while testing with the arm. At the same time have your client hit the toes of her feet together twice then bring the toes forward twice. **(Figure 9-3)** Finally, do the same thing with the left hand while still holding the breath. When you test, you should find a clear response.

The second technique is much simpler. While your client is lying on her back take the middle finger of your left hand and the forefinger of your right hand and place them on the top of her head. The middle finger left hand goes on the "soft-spot" of the head and the forefinger of the right hand goes about one-and-a-half inches forward on the head. **(Figure 9-4)** Have her take a deep breath holding it as long as possible thinking about the problem state. What you are feeling for is your client's heartbeat synchronizing through the major blood vessels on the top of the head. **(Figure 9-5)** When the pulsing is synchronized the realignment is complete. When you test you should find it clear.

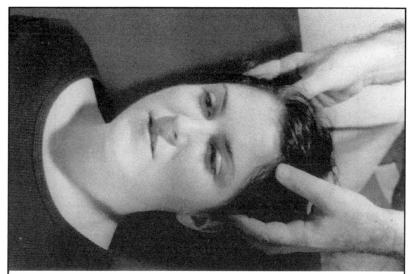

Figure 9-1

Rubbing the Scalp for
Resource Realigning Technique

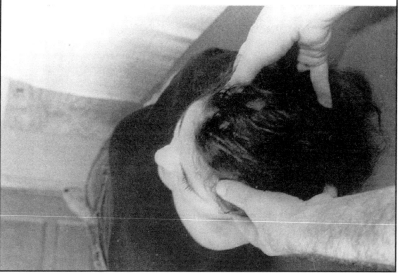

Make sure that your hands are rubbing the lobes of the brain.
Rub for about one minute.

Figure 9-2   Testing for the Problem State

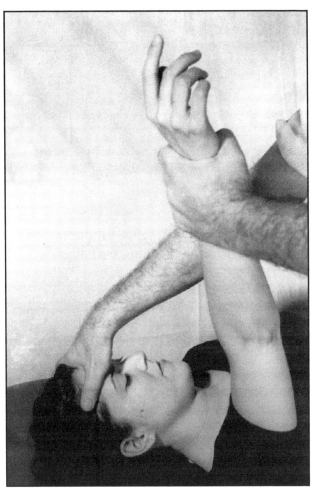

Make sure that your client has taken a deep breath and
is holding her breath while you test the Problem State.

Figure 9-3   Tapping the Feet and Bringing them Forward
                            Twice for the Realigning Process

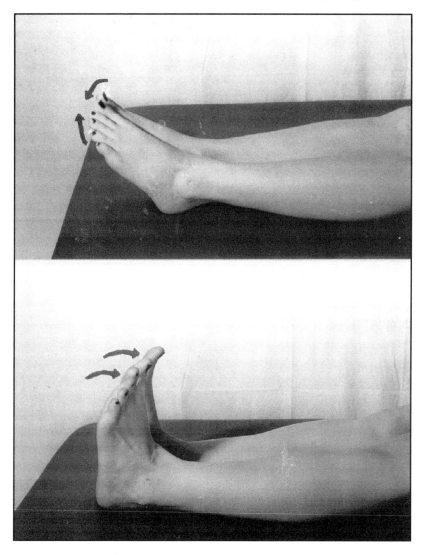

Figure 9-4   The Finger Position for the Resource
                                                        Realigning

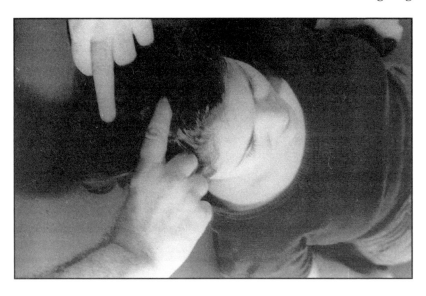

Figure 9-5

The Blood Vessels
on the Head

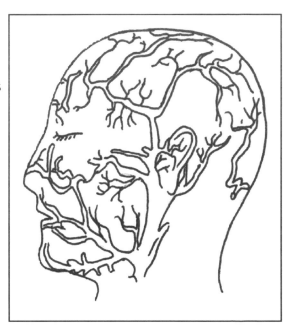

The third technique is rather simple as well. Have your client sit up. On the three phases of respiration you will tap the T-8 vertebrae three times. The T-8 is approximately at the end of the rib cage. **(Figure 9-6)** Have your client think of the problem and take a deep breath and tap T-8. Then have her exhale and tap again. Finally, have her hold no breath in the lungs and tap again. It should be clear when the testing is done.

The final technique is another simple one as well. Have your client lying on her back. Place your thumb and little finger along the center-line of her forehead about one-half inch or so above the center of the eyebrows. **(Figure 9-7)** Have your client close her eyes, take a deep breath and hold it thinking about the problem state, and roll her eyes around in one direction then in the other direction. While she is doing this you will tap your fingers on the top of her forehead twice while her eyes are rolling in one direction and twice as the eyes are rolling in the other direction. When you test, it should be cleared.

The last thing to do is to say to your client: "Think about (problem state)" and test. It should be weak. Then state: "Think about this healing. Hold." The test should be strong. Now you are ready to go on to the next step.

Figure 9-6   Tapping the T-8 Vertebrae
                                        for the Resource Realigning

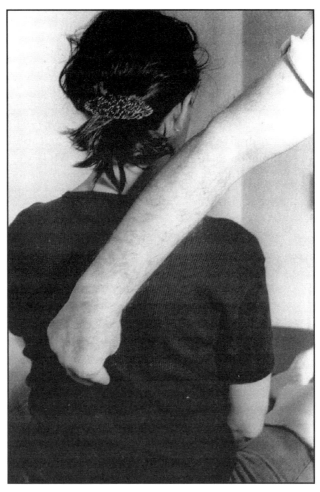

The T-8 is found by going to the center of the back down
the spinal column and counting about two inches more.
The tap doesn't have to be hard but it needs to be solid.
Remember that you must tap on the three phases of
respiration.

Figure 9-7   The Frontal Brain Resource Realigning

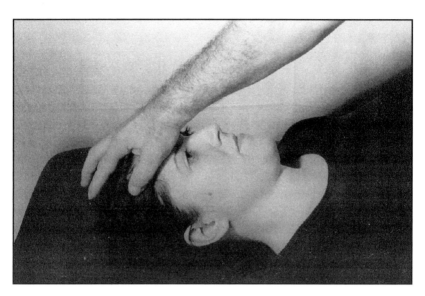

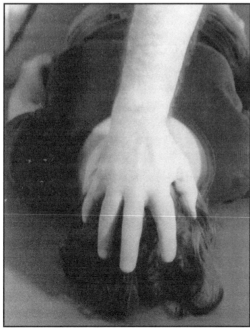

Make sure that you have your client roll her eyes in a circle while doing this Realigning procedure.

CHAPTER 10

ADVANCING THE HEALING

What good is affecting change in one instance if it is not useful outside of that instance? This is a major problem in most traditional and group therapies. Quite often therapists have noticed that a client can make nice changes in a group or in therapy sessions but that change does not generalize into the real world. This becomes a source of frustration for both the client and therapist and tends to keep the client in therapy longer than is necessary.

There are some traditional therapies which do progress the change into the future. One of these is Rational-Emotive Behavioral Therapy, a cognitive therapy developed by Albert Ellis, Ph.D. The practice of progressing the change into the future is termed "rational imagery." In rational imagery the client is instructed to visualize the problematic situation exactly as it was experienced with all of its emotions in tact all the way to the end. After that is done then the client is told to go back to the beginning and start to run through the same experience all the way until a "choice-point" is reached. Once here the client chooses another response and runs it through to the end. After this has been completed the therapist asks, "What did you tell yourself to get the change?" This may be done several times. What rational imagery does is to get the client to begin to look for more choices available and consider them. Consequently, when confronted by the same or a similar situation the client will not immediately do the same thing as (s)he had habitually done. Neuro-Linguistic Programming has a process which they call "future-pacing." The general future-pacing technique is nothing more than much the same process as rational imagery except that the choice of the different reaction is made before the visual imagery is done. Both of these techniques work more on the conscious level dealing with conscious choice. Also both of these advancing techniques make their system more effective than those therapies which do not use any sort of future progressing at all.

Time is a human concept and does not actually exist universally. This is one of the reasons that time is considered relative. If you will recall when you were a child time seemed to drag between birthdays and other holidays where you would receive gifts. Then, as you grew older the years passed so quickly that it seemed almost obscene. Physicists find time and space both extremely difficult to measure. The only way to do it is to compare it with something else. An example is comparing the time that the Milky Way Galaxy, the Sun and the Earth have been existing. Time, then, is a product of *conscious experience* and conscious experience requires a *frame of reference* from which to exist. Consequently, most overt learning occurred in a step-by-step fashion using specific frames of references, or cues, in order to be expressed. This puts the learning *inside of time*. Once learned, it becomes unconscious and, consequently, *outside of time*.

The *Time Progression* technique makes use of this natural process. Since the unconscious mind has no specific frame of reference for its experience it can be modified much easier than the conscious mind. Since the unconscious does not require a frame of reference and generalizes much easier than the conscious, unconscious processes can be adjusted much easier.

One of the most important aspects of *Psychokinesiology* is that of *Time Progression*. You already have the technique for *Time Reversal* in order to find the *Time of Origin* of a problem. Now you will be able to do the reverse and take the healing change forward into the future.

There are certain presuppositions made with the *Time Progression* technique. The first presupposition is that the unconscious mind has no sense of time. That is one reason that *Time Reversal* and *Time Progression* are possible. Since you can take the unconscious back in time it is also possible to go forward. The key theory behind *Time Progression* is that once the resources have been realigned the unconscious is already changing how it is responding to the formerly problematic situation. Like a series of dominos, once the beginning of the problem has been adjusted there is an automatic change in subsequently associated experiences. This does not mean that the experiences themselves have been changed. What has changed is the perspective that the unconscious has taken. This automatically shifts resources because the preceding resources are not able to function as previously because they have been recomplexed. *Recomplexing* simply means that the *behaviors associated with a particular complex have been either changed and new ones added or strategically readjusted.* Consequently, *nothing* is taken away.

Another presupposition is that the *Time Progression* technique works instantly because the unconscious mind learns immediately. Then by progressing that learning forward through time the change becomes permanent and generative. The speed at which the unconscious learns is one of the key elements in the *Time Progression* technique and in *Psychokinesiology* itself. The unconscious associates ideas and experiences instantly and when change has been installed at the *Time of Origin* of a problem behavior similar behavioral problems are likewise affected by the change.

Many people think that all learning requires a step-by-step procedure. There is quite a bit of research to show that learning occurs on many levels and that experiences such as *state dependent* and *context dependent* learning exist. *State dependent learning* means that a *person must initiate a specific state of mind or consciousness for a learning experience and must be in the same state in order to repeat it. Context dependent learning* means that *an individual learns a particular behavior in a specific context (e.g. location) and finds it easiest to repeat the learning when in that context.* All learning is the process of teaching the neurons of the brain to respond at a specific time and to a specific cue. *Resource Realigning* takes this learning and readjusts the time and cue. The *Time Progression* takes this time and cue and associates it with similar responses within the unconscious thus shifting one's response ability. Since the unconscious has no sense of time and that it does not remember anything in a specific time sequence or order the *Time Progression* is able to reorder and re-sequence the previously problematic behaviors.

The *Time Progression* technique creates shifts in consciousness affecting both state dependent and context dependent learning experiences. Anything which had been learned in a specific state or context and the associated generalizations to them will be altered because of the shift in consciousness. This shift comes about because of the change in the original state or context. As this shift is brought forward through time all of the other associated generalizations will be shifted as well thus altering the consciousness even more.

A third presupposition is that the unconscious will automatically find and attach the appropriate resources to the problem behavior. This will shift the behavior from one that is a limitation and gets in the way to one that is more effective and useful. It will have the tendency to reframe the experience thus affording a different perspective to the problem behavior.

A fourth presupposition is that *Resource Realigning* technique spontaneously creates a fully-functioning feedback loop within unconscious parts as well as between the conscious and the unconscious. This feedback loop is automatically self-correcting and functions on a higher level than previously. Doing a *Time Progression* is one of the best ways of testing to insure that this feedback loop and the change you have brought about is available as a resource. It is wise after the *Time Progression* that you ask your client what other options (s)he now sees available in that situation. Invariably, you will have an affirmative response. You will notice that the main response in Pk is unconscious. Consequently, *Time Progression* is likewise on the unconscious level. By asking your client what other options are now open you are bringing some of those unconscious resources to the conscious level. This can insure a more appropriate response. It will also give your client the conscious awareness of where the change has come from. Often, if this conscious awareness is not in place, the change can be attributed to just about anything.

The next presupposition is that the *Time Progression* will realign the resources even more as your client is brought into the future with the shifts which occur through time. What happens then is that individual strategies for performing different behaviors are changed by the unconscious itself. This changes the experience in the mind and places it on a different level.

The sixth presupposition is that all learning and behavior is the result of changes in neurological patterns. Once the original neurological patterns have been adjusted then a *Time Progression* readjusts the new patterns making them work even more effectively. The new changes are integrated into the system and conscious behavioral change is the result. What *Time Progression* does is teach the unconscious to interact with its own resources and experiences in more and better ways. This increases individual flexibility.

A seventh presupposition is that *Time Progression* is a way of creating unconscious repetitions of a new pattern. As you are progressing your client forward in time the unconscious is automatically choosing new ways of responding as if the person had a different state of awareness from the beginning. This is why you can ask your client to state different choices which are available...and you will get them. Consequently, the more repetitions that happen the more change occurs, building in flexibility.

Flexibility in behavior occurs when internal elements have been reorganized into a different pattern. This broadens the scope of how an individual looks at what (s)he had been doing. When these elements are reorganized into a different pattern then the meaning of the experience changes. Thus, different choices are made available.

The eighth presupposition in *Time Progression* is that internal experience is considered to be as significant behaviorally as overt measurable responses. In other words, it is not necessary to spend a lot of time changing behavior or readjusting semantics. The *Time Progression* done internally will automatically do that. You will recall that the brain does not know the difference between a physically real or imagined event. It acts *as if* both are the same. Consequently, with each *Time Progression* the brain is acting *as if* the activity is being performed and new learning has occurred.

The last *Time Progression* presupposition is that this process produces an automatic *generative* change. As you take your client forward in time with the change the unconscious spontaneously creates change as if it had already occurred. Then, as you will see, this change is brought to the present complete.

The *Time Progression* technique is a way of taking your client from where they are to the best place for them to go, not just where they want to be. There are times that where a person wants to be is not the best place for them. Since the unconscious is able to see things in a different manner than the conscious it is able make associations that the conscious cannot possibly understand. As this is done your client will find subtle behavioral and emotional changes which will direct him/her into the best place. Since there are feedback loops within the different parts of the unconscious and between the conscious and unconscious there will be a subtle motivation toward the best possible experience. It is interesting to note that many of your clients will have presupposed that change has already occurred once you have performed the *Time Progression* technique.

At the end of the last chapter we ended with you saying to your client: "Think about (<u>problem state</u>)" and testing the statement. It should be weak. Then state: "Think about this healing." Testing this statement should get a strong response. Now you are ready to take the healing up in time. You may consider at this time a *Retrograde Polarity* statement: "Think about (<u>problem state</u>)" and "Think about (<u>opposite state</u>)." You should have a weak and strong response respectively.

You will recall that the *Time Reversal* technique involved tapping the *Thymus Point* and stating something like: "Think about (<u>problem state</u>) five years ago" and continue on back to the *Time of Origin*. Now that you have done a *Resource Realigning* you will do the reverse in order to bring the healing up in time. For example, if you found the *Time of Origin* of the problem state was at the third month in utero, after you have done the realigning tap the *Thymus Point* and state: "Bring this healing up to your birth, and hold." The test should be strong. Then continue progressing the healing up to the present time. Each test should be strong. Once you get to the present take the healing forward. State: "Take this healing into tomorrow, and hold." The test should be strong. Continue on in this manner: "Take this healing into (<u>next week, next month, next year, ten years from now, fifty years from now</u>)," testing each one. Once you have gone sufficiently into the future then state: "Bring this healing back to the present, and hold." You will get a strong response.

With this last test you have brought the healing from the past into the future and back to the present. Along with the healing you have brought resources and other choices based on a different past experience as well as a different future. It is this *Time Progression* process which sets up the unconscious to make changes.

After you have brought the healing back to the present the next thing for you to do is to have your client put her hand on her forehead in the same manner as previously for the inquiry into clearing. Have your client state: "*This* one is healed," and test. The test should be strong. Then state: "There is more to do on *that* one." The test should be weak.

Assuming that you have the appropriate strong and weak responses, end with: "This one is healed," and test again. The test will be strong.

If you get a weak response when your client states the first "This one is healed" or "There is more to do on that one" it is necessary to do some further checking. Begin by asking: "Yes or no, do we need more information before this can be realigned? Hold." You will most likely get a strong response. Then ask: "Yes or no, do we need to clear an emotion? Hold." If you get a weak response then go down through other checks such as beliefs, attitudes, and behaviors. If an emotion needs to be cleared then ask if the emotion is fear, anxiety, anger, helplessness, guilt, or hurt. Then, whether you found an emotion or belief or so on ask: "Yes or no, do we need to find the *Time of Origin* of this (emotion, belief, etc.)? Hold." If so, then do a *Time Reversal*. If not ask: "Yes or no, do we need to know whose (emotion, belief, etc.) this was? Hold." If you get a strong response then find out if it was immediate family (mother, father, or sibling), other relative (grandparent, uncle, aunt, cousin), peer or friend, teacher, etc. Then ask: "Yes or no, do we need to find out when this (emotion, belief, etc.) was installed? Hold." If you get a weak response ask: "Yes or no, do we have enough information to clear this now? Hold." If you get a strong response, clear it. If you get a weak response you will probably need to do a *Time Reversal* and clear it. Then test it with a *Retrograde Polarity* and do a *Time Progression* on it. Often when you get a weak response on the statement: "There is more to do on that one." It may be because you had not found the actual problem state that needs clearing. Other times it is because your client may have gotten confused because (s)he thought that it was necessary to think of a response when you were going through your statements or had not kept his/her mind on the problem state during the *Resource Realigning*. Another reason that you may get a weak response with the above statement is because your client did not hold his/her breath or did not hold the breath long enough. When the breath is not held or not held long enough it is an indicator that your client is resisting the change. The fact is that if your client does not hold the breath or does not hold it long enough you will usually know when you test immediately after the *Resource Realigning* procedure. If you get a strong response when the breath is not held long enough it indicates that something has been changed. Then when you state: "There is more to do on that one" and you get a strong response you will know what to do.

The thing to remember is that people do not respond to their environment. They are responding to the *labels* that they use to *describe* their environment. After you have done the *Resource Realigning* and the *Time Progression* you are getting the unconscious to change its labels. Once the labels are changed the interpretation of what is happening in the environment is different and so will be the response to the environment.

CHAPTER 11

ECOLOGICAL CHECK

How often is it that once a therapeutic intervention has been completed a check is made to insure that other psychic parts of the individual are in harmony with the change? It is quite obvious that if there are parts of your client which do not agree with the adjustment the change will either not take place or will be only partially successful and you will be going over the same thing again. So, it is necessary to make sure that what you do is holistically sound and is going to last.

To be ecologically sound means that the complete system is going to operate effectively and in a positive way the next time the problematic situation appears. Remember that the human psyche is a *system*. This system contains all of the learning experiences; all of the positive and negative relationships with the environment. Contained in the system are all of what was gleaned vicariously and through trial and error or otherwise from other people's relationships with their environment. Finally there are the ideals, beliefs, and value constructs of your client and of those with whom he has come into contact with. Lest we forget, there are also the genetic influences and predispositions. This system operates perfectly for what it is doing when it is doing it. This means that due to the individual's physiological and psychic construction what that person is doing, what he chooses, his beliefs, attitudes, and values are who that person is. He could not be otherwise. The implication is that this individual is operating as he *should* be operating. When there is a problem state this indicates that some part of the system is either not operating to its fullest capacity or is not fully or not precisely connected with the other parts or to its own resources. A problem state indicates that the individual is not evolving in some area(s) and is viewing his relationship with his environment or himself in an unchanging way which interferes with his life and living experiences.

The whole concept of ecology involves the interconnectedness of all of the psychic parts of the individual. Every individual's psyche is not a single entity but a fragmented pattern of experiences and influences. Each of these experiences and influences interacts with each other. Each of the experiences also has a series of accompanying resources and behavioral predispositions and emotional presets as well as other psychic processes connected to it. Then the whole system operates as a unit incorporating resources from some of the other parts which may be related in some way to it.

Psychic ecology is akin to the ecology of nature. Every part of nature is connected with every other part of nature either directly or indirectly and, hence, every part of nature is dependent upon every other part of nature. Whenever a single and simple change occurs in the physical environment these changes affect the next level and the next level and so on. Then after many years the whole environment changes. With these changes some portions of the physical environment will become extinct while others evolve becoming different.

A similar process occurs in the human psyche whether the individual's psyche is operating in a unified harmony or not. All parts of the person operate according to their installation and structure. Some will work well in specific contexts while others will not. If the person continues to use parts which are not working well the system will not evolve. Once he decides to do something about the problematic behaviors and makes changes, then like nature itself, the system begins to evolve and change. Every individual operates properly for his experiences and inheritance. He is not broken in any way. Everything works. The problems occur when the resources that the person has are not operating appropriately. With constructive evolution parts which had gotten in the person's way are no longer getting in his way. Other parts evolve to work better in and with the system. Still other parts change their relationship with the system as a whole. What we see here is that the psyche is a unified, harmonious whole.

Psychokinesiology is an holistic process. It assumes that the individual is a complete system. It works through the whole system correcting both conscious and unconscious operations. In traditional psychotherapies there tends to be more conscious reconstruction. That is, the reconstruction process is based on external, mainly verbal, repatterning. The assumption is made that if an individual is able to discuss a problem state in a particular way then change has occurred. It is then up to the individual to incorporate the change into his life.

In *Psychokinesiology* every part of the client is connected to every other part of the client and it all operates synergistically. There is no separation between the inner thoughts your client has and his outer experience. The personality is seen as a unified whole based on genetic inheritance and innumerable and fragmented incidents and events which the individual had encountered and were integrated into the whole. The whole system is operating perfectly for what it is. If a behavior, an attitude, a value, or belief is not operating properly in a specific situation it is not because the behavior is wrong or does not work or that there is something wrong with the person. It is because it is operating *out of time, out of place, out of state,* or *out of order*. What this means is that the operation is either temporally, contextually, contentually, or sequentially dysfunctional. When a behavior, belief, or so on is *temporally dysfunctional* it means that the *timing* is the problem. When a person's timing is off the individual will make choices which arc cithcr too early, not taking everything into account, or too late by waiting too long before making a decision. An example is coming up with an idea which is ahead of its time. An idea which is ahead of its time does not get appreciated in the period in which it is expressed. If an operation is *contextually dysfunctional* the choice does not fit the *conditions* under which it is operating. A person who is laughing during a serious experience is operating emotionally out of place. This reaction may be due to fear, lack of awareness of the situation, or any number of other reasons. An example of a *contentually dysfunctional* operation is a non-sequitur statement. This generally indicates that the person has not understand the *meaning* of the situation, is not following the flow of the thought, or has an incorrect conception of what is happening or being discussed. One who is operating with a *sequential dysfunction* is one whose internal organization or *order* for decisions for behaviors is organized in such a way that it gets in his way causing frustration and emotional problems. What this means is that the individual has a specific pattern of cues (strategy) that he pays attention to before acting in a certain way and continues this action even if it is not useful or even if the cues are temporally separated.

In order to get an individual operating appropriately all that needs to be done is to *readjust* or *resequence the operations*. This may seem like a rather difficult task but as you have seen, the realigning process is what does this resequencing. Once the resequencing has been accomplished then a check must be done to insure that all of the systems will be operating in accordance with the change.

The individual is an *evolving system*. It is necessary that the natural process of evolution be incorporated in with the change. *Psychokinesiology* is a *generative* process meaning as one part of the system is adjusted other parts which are related to it are automatically modified thus generating new responses. In essence, this generative process is a *chain* of adjustments. This chain can be likened to the semantic tree which comprises the major associational processing of the brain. **(Figure 11-1)** The semantic tree begins with one idea, concept, belief, behavior, or so forth and brings together many other relationships. Each of the related ideas is essentially a *complex* which has accompanying behaviors, beliefs, and value systems with it. This chain uses the more useful aspects and resources of the new state. Like a computer program, as one portion of the state is triggered and begins functioning more appropriately, it reconnects with the resource states which it and other related states have in order to more properly operate in the situation. This modification generates new perspectives and brings other resources into line with the change. Once the new chain has been installed the result is more and better choices and resources available to your client.

There are mainly four stages in life through which we evolve psychologically, emotionally, mentally, and socially. The first stage is childhood. In the earliest portion of this stage the individual is initially operating from a reflexive standpoint being that he is behaving as is his nature. As he matures then he is influenced by his external environment. It is this external environment which adjusts his reflexive nature to behave more appropriately within a social context. The individual learns his values, beliefs, attitudes, morality, and basic life's responses during childhood. These responses tend to stay with him throughout life. The second stage is adolescence. With the changes at the beginning of puberty an internal biochemical energy replaces some of the environmental

Figure 11-1   The Semantic Tree

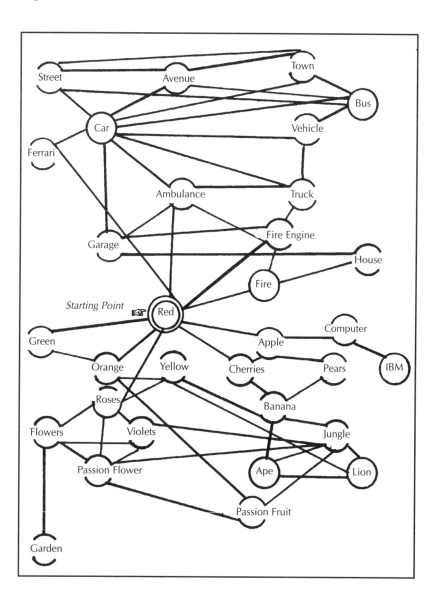

influences. The individual begins to see life differently being highly influenced by the chemical changes occurring throughout the body. This affects the previous learning and his views of that experience. The third stage is that of adulthood. It was at one time thought that there were no changes after adolescence such as those occurring at puberty. Researchers know this not to be true. Physiological, biochemical, and psychological, changes continue to occur. At this stage it is assumed that the individual has learned much from previous experience and has the ability to make viable choices. If you will look at the choices that most adults make you can see that this is certainly *not* true. Most people are still making choices and operating from a middle/late childhood model of life. Their beliefs are based on childhood models and representations of the universe. This can be seen in the vehement ways that many people defend and want to impose their own ideas and unrealistic belief systems on to others. Their values, attitudes, and moral behaviors are ego-centered and unrealistic. Often in adulthood you will find discussion centering on morality and values. The morality and values being discussed are not based on universal morals and values which promote the freedom to think and to search but on a convoluted sense of right and wrong which come from a childhood conception of life: "What is true for me is true for you and you must accept it." You will also find many adult's emotional reactions being wholly inappropriate and less than useful. Many of these reactions are nothing more than displaced and layered reactions learned from early models of emotional responding. The final stage of life is late adulthood. This is the period of time when life's evolution is to reach its apex. All of the experiences that one has had come together and wisdom is supposed to be the result. This does not always occur. It is so unfortunate when someone in this final stage of life feels unfulfilled, bitter, lonely, and unhappy. This is to be a time of reflection upon personal evolution. Being unfulfilled indicates that there is a lot of regret for the choices made and for things not done. The main reason for this regret is emotional overreaction due to holding on to fears, unrealistic models of life, constricting belief systems, and self-centered morals and values. All of these restrict personal evolution.

All of the stages of life have their effect on the evolving personality. If left as is the individual personality has little room to evolve beyond its natural ability to respond. It will continue operating in a more or less reflexive nature learning not much more than the basic difference between pleasure and pain. The influence of others, the society, the media, and what has been personally learned greatly modify the reflexive nature of the personality. By learning from life's experiences the individual will be able to grow and change without having to repeat problem situations again.

We experience change not in great leaps and bounds but in small steps and shifts both inside and outside. We know that change has occurred once we notice that something is different about ourself and what is happening in our life. Since we human beings are experts in the use of the process of generalization a simple change can be generalized into more complex experiences and this most specifically happens in small steps.

Psychokinesiology operates using those subtle variations of which major change is comprised and it works with the individual's natural process of evolution. In this way your client can be more directly involved in his own personal change naturally. What brings the individual to become more directly involved in his own evolution is the process of choice. After a *Resource Realigning* your client will notice that something deep inside has been changed. He is able to look at problem states from different perspectives and because of that is able to come up with more and different choices in each situation. It is interesting how after a *Resource Realigning* session this uncomplicated ability to make different choices seems simply *natural*.

Each individual's personality is a fifty-fifty interaction. This means that fifty percent of the personality is genetic and fifty percent is environmental. You will recall that the fifty percent which is genetic is mainly *predispositions* to act, to feel, and to think in certain ways. It is the environmental experience which turns these predispositions into actual behaviors while adding to these predispositions its own perceptions. Every part of our personality is a learning experience and a combination of heredity and environment. In every stage of life our personality evolves based on the differences in perception for that time. It is most unfortunate that many people are still operating from a childhood model of life *without* engaging the process of evolution. This is one of the main reasons that behaviors, thoughts, values, and emotional reactions are inappropriate for the time, the place, and the state.

Most often we consider that the reason for our emotional (over)reaction is because of what is going on outside of ourself. Many people feel that due to external situations they are restricted as to what they can and cannot do. Statements like: "If it wasn't for _____ I'd be a success" or "My boss keeps me from getting a better position" and so forth indicate an individual sees an external locus of control. What happens to us in life is *influenced* by external circumstances when in actuality what is going on *inside* is the key element to how we react to what is happening outside. The fact of the matter is that what is going on inside of you *is* based on what *had* happened on the outside. Whatever you are feeling now is determined by the specific perceptions and thought processes that you have engaged at the present. This is based on your past, especially on past learning experiences and past *choices*. All of these choices are based upon a sort of synergistic ecology. If the choices result in a positive relationship with the external environment then the system appears to be ecologically sound. When the choices result in emotional overreactions, frustration, hostility, fears, and so forth there is a problem with the system. In actuality even if the choices are getting in your way in some areas of life there is a kind of synergy. When working with a client what you need to look at is if the person on some level actually *wants* what they are claiming they do not want. If this is so then the system is operating as it is supposed to be operating. In the Individual Psychology of Alfred Adler and in some theoretical views in cognitive psychology the neurotic is defined as someone who feels that he *must* suffer. These feelings of suffering quite often are based on the belief that what is being experienced is the best there is for them and that is all they deserve. If this is occurring in your client's life then it is obvious that the system is operating synergistically. To understand this synergy look at the reward system that your client has. You will do this in your initial questioning in order to find out what needs to be cleared. The reward system will tell you who is controlling what in your client's environment.

To insure that your client is ecologically sound means that your client will have his ability to make different choices engaged and operating more efficiently. The parts which are slightly amiss and not operating as effectively as they could will be brought in line with the situation allowing for a better set of choices being made. To have a sound system ecology means that there is a synergistic ebb and flow of energy between conscious experience and unconscious parts.

Checking for system ecology is a most important part of the *Psychokinesiology* process. The ecology check insures that all of the psychic parts of your client are achieving a clearer relationship with each other and with the resources that your client has. The ultimate test for ecology is to place your client in the same problem state and watch for the change. This is not always possible immediately after a session. The next best thing is to do some internal checks. It is these internal checks which will tell you if what you have just completed is harmonizing the whole system.

There are several ecology checks in *Psychokinesiology*. One thing that you can do is after you have brought your client back to the present in the *Future Progression* simply ask: "Yes or no, is there anything which is getting in the way of this change taking place?" and test. If you get a positive response then you can go back and check if it is an emotion, a belief, a value, or an attitude. Most often you will get an emotion as the stumbling block. Check again if the emotion is fear, anxiety, anger, helplessness, hopelessness and so on. Then check to see if you can do a *Resource Realigning* to clear it or if you need to find the *Time of Origin* for it. Then continue on as normally. The chances are, that you will not need to do this at all because going back to the *Time of Origin* and doing your *Resource Realigning* then bringing the healing up to the present, into the future, and back into the present will adjust the system most effectively.

The next ecology check is by having your client state a *Retrograde Polarity* regarding the change. You can run through the whole series of statements: want, need, allow, let, and so on to find out if there is any one of them that gets a weak response. If you do get a weak response you can do as was described in the previous paragraph.

The best ecology check is simply going back to the *Emotional Reflex Points* and checking the point where the energy was centered and blocked. You will remember that when you first checked the *Emotional Reflex Point* you got a weak response and then you tested to find which emotion(s) were being blocked at that point. After you did the *Resource Realigning* you found that the response was strong. So you took this new response into a *Time Progression*. Now, when you make a new test on the organ point you should find the response strong. What you can also do after that is to have your client think of the healing and test each of the *Emotional Reflex Points*. You may get a weak response with one of them. This would indicate another emotion that may need to be dealt with at this time. Another thing that you may do is to have your client think of the original problem and test the *Emotional Reflex Points*. The chances are very high that once the *Resource Realigning* has been completed and a *Time Progression* has been done you will not have to do anything else.

After you have done your ecology check a real convincer that something has happened internally is this: Tap the *Thymus Point* and state: "It is a half hour before you got here. Think about (the problem state)." Test this and you will get a strong response. Then tap the *Thymus Point* and state: "Come back to the present and think about (the problem state)." Test this and you will get a weak response. You can test the healing by stating again: "Think about this healing." You will get a strong response. Once your client sees this the conscious mind can see that something has happened. From this your client will quickly learn to associate the positive changes that will be occurring in his life to the *Psychokinesiology* session.

Final Word

The noted hypnotherapist Milton Erickson said that therapy is like starting a snowball rolling down a mountain. Once started it builds up momentum and can grow into an avalanche. All the therapist has to do is to start the ball rolling. In essence, a therapist needs to find a way to get the process to begin. After that the individual's internal systems will take over from there.

Therapy consists of a process of change which is consciously and deliberately entered into between a therapist and the client. This process needs to be designed to achieve mutually desired results. In order for this process to be effective the therapist must secure a client's agreement to undergo change. It is necessary that there be the client's conscious and unconscious commitment and agreement otherwise change is not easily achieved.

For any therapy to be effective it must be made compatible with the client's social and personal values and beliefs. This is what is meant by being ecologically sound. The reason this is so important is because beliefs limit unconscious resources. Whatever the client believes about him/herself, his/her life and what (s)he deserves from life will affect external behaviors, relationships, and the roles that the individual will assume as well as how those roles will be played out.

Social roles are sets of communications and behaviors. They limit our ability to communicate with others. Whatever role we acquire will dictate the behaviors and communications we will express while assuming that role. Acquiring new ways of communication can affect the way a role is played. If a whole pattern of communications of a role is missing it will limit the performance of that social role.

Social roles shape our communications with others. The role through which we are raised shapes our perceptions. This role limits our control and the range of communications possible.What therapy has been seen as is the acquisition of a new social role. This role expands the client's ability to communicate and respond in the environment.

People come by problems due to faulty or insufficient learning, or the inability to utilize the learning already acquired. Many problems occur as discrepancies between beliefs and unconscious resources and behaviors. Internal conflicts originate as interpersonal conflicts. That is, as a child we see how our parents behave toward each other, their attitudes toward other people (verbally stated beliefs, values, stated or implied needs, and perceptual predispositions), and their attitudes and behaviors toward us and we assume that what they are doing is the appropriate behavior. In essence, we have no other frame of reference. Once in the world we find that some things that we learned work and some things do not. This causes role confusion and behaviors are acquired which approximate the role behavior.

People experience stressors as part of everyday life. Their ability to adapt or contend with stressors determines their ability to mobilize them. When persons perceive stressors as challenging they are able to mobilize resources. If they see them as "overwhelming" it becomes difficult to make any changes. All clients, even those "thinking for themselves" have painted themselves into a corner, a small limited area of life where they feel comfortable. This comfort zone is the area of certainty where they can fully predict as much as possible. This comfort zone becomes a specific theoretical lens used in order to maintain a problem.

A problem can be defined by appearance, function, etiology, history, or its relationship to other things. A person will report problems when there is, first of all, a modified awareness or a change which brings the problem to the forefront. Secondly, there is or can be an altered intensity from the normal desire state with personal needs not being met or fulfilled. Third, there is or can be a determined act of will where the individual notices a problem and intentionally does something about it. Fourth, there can be a personal understanding being reached. Finally there is a particular situation being defined as a problem

People tend to continue in their problematic behavior until something happens. An individual is not going to notice a problem until certain characteristic symptoms are present. These include:

1. an intense focusing on the painful sensations and (s)he is seemingly unable to ignore them;

2. an altered intensity of emotional experience (e.g. a change in mood such as depression or fear);
3. an unintentional experience occurs so that the "symptom just happens." The situation is out of the client's control so (s)he does not feel like he did anything to cause it;
4. an unintentional reaction seems to occur (e.g. "I go crazy when he does that");
5. situations being defined as problems (a problem for one person is a challenge for another).

There are five processes which will hold a problem in place. These processes are unconscious and often the reason for their being is long since gone. They have become habitual and tend to be generalized to anything which may seem similar to the original inducer. The *first* of these processes is that of *conflicting motivations*. This means that the individual is torn apart inside. This is what is termed here as a *Retrograde Polarity* or the cognitive dissonance of psychology. You will recall that one part of the *Retrograde Polarity* is an internal conflict where a person wants to have and does not want to have the same thing. The other part is where the person wants one thing and its opposite at the same time. The conflict develops and stagnation results.

Whenever we are considering conflicting motivators we need to look at another psychological concept. That is the approach/avoidance conflict. There are three levels of the approach/avoidance conflict. The first is approach/avoidance. Here the conflict is between one thing that is attractive and one that is not. A decision is quite easy in this instance. The second level is that of avoidance/avoidance. Here we have two equally unattractive things. A choice becomes a little more complicated. The last level is that of approach/approach when there are two equally compelling things. A decision becomes extremely difficult. "What if..." becomes the key to not making a decision: "What if I take this and I find out that the other one is better?" As long as an individual continues with conflicting ideas (s)he will never make the changes necessary.

The *second process* holding the problem in place is that of *compromise*. This can be defined as settling for what you can get. This means that you will get into your comfort zone and stay there choosing not to make any decisions or making any changes. What you have now is the best that there is. The *third process* holding the problem in place is your silent rules. These are the expectations, beliefs, and personal demands on yourself and others. Included here are the roles that you play as well as the behaviors and cognitions associated with them. The *fourth of these processes* are your *values, dependencies, and boundaries.* These boundaries include your own self-accepted boundaries and the boundaries that you place on your relations with others. The *last process* holding problems in place is *permission seeking.* In essence, this means that you are constantly seeking the approval of others. If you find that someone, anyone, does not approve you will not feel that it is appropriate to make the particular choice. Recall that all of these are unconscious responses. Consequently, the person's approval that you most want need not even be alive. That person exists only in your own mind and it is impossible to please that person.

All problems have to be maintained. At some level active energy is needed to maintain the problem. The fact of the matter is that problems are self-maintaining. This means that the problem is in itself rewarding. It could be the secondary gain from assuming others are approving of it. This assumption can be from nothing more than supposing someone's sympathy toward the problem. It can be self-rewarding because it goes along with something that we had learned decades ago about ourself ("You'll never amount to much"). The mechanism by which the problem is maintained is perceived as outside of awareness.

Whenever a client comes to you with a problem look for symptoms that protect a homeostasis. Just like the physical body, our psychological and emotional systems need to stay in harmony. Look for deletion, distortion, and generalizations as the main processes maintaining the homeostasis. Find the generalizations and change them in some way (i.e. reframe them or readjust the resources). This will bring about a shift and still maintain the homeostasis.

Whether or not we are aware of it each one of us "votes" on every life experience. This vote either values or devalues the experience. This installs it as either a friend or enemy, a resource or defect. It is assumed that the way a person relates to a phenomenon determines its value and the response to it. Such methods seek to transpose problems into solutions by changing the way a person "votes" on an experience. The shift from a self-devaluation to a self-valuation brings about change. In essence, if the rules are changed the organization is changed.

The main goal of therapy is to get the person out of therapy. The conclusion of a successful therapeutic relationship is evidence that the client has reached a level of individuation appropriate for accepting and managing the ongoing interaction between the self and the world.

The expressed goals of therapy are to:

1. Identify the specific values within a client that are expressive of his/her uniqueness. Look for those talents, abilities, skills and special faculties that may be unexpressed.

2. Accept the identified values as valid for that client. A person's values denote their feelings of self-worth. Where these feelings of self-worth are placed will help you to focus on the strengths and weakness of your client.

3. Translate these values into multiple dimensions of experience, especially behavior.

To assume that the client already has the know-how needed to solve the problem makes your job so much easier. The client already has all (s)he needs to make the changes necessary. Therapy should be the key to help her realize her own possibilities. Engaging those special talents, skills, abilities and so on will redirect all of his/her inner resources and bring about the change. To bring this about focus on what is changeable. Look for solutions and abilities rather than pathology.

Every client has set up a series of expectations which will direct their behaviors. These expectations are expressed as silent rules. In order to understand a client's silent rules you need to understand his/her emotional expectations. Many of these expectations are directed at the therapist. The therapist needs to be highly sensitive to these expectations. They will come across in the emotional climate that the client sets up that serve his/her purposes.

Traditionally the therapist's treatment plan has reflected the belief that the longer the treatment, the better it will be for the client. This comes from the mistaken idea that it took the client a long time to get where she is so it is necessary to go through a long and drawn-out deconstruction and reconstruction. It has been assumed that this is the best method to get more normal functioning. Study after study has shown that this method is not the best. One reason is that it is extremely inefficient and is extremely inelegant.

Therapy involves the creation of new memories (Time Progression). These memories are changes in how the client views the previously problematic situations. It is important that as a therapist you do what is necessary to promote therapeutic or growth experiences. One of the most effective means of doing this is through kindness and humor. Kindness and humor have been largely ignored by traditional therapy. There is a belief that the client is there because (s)he is extremely troubled. In order to be most effective the therapist must be aloof to be objective and must be serious because this is a serious problem. What this does is creates an environment where rapport and trust take entirely too long to develop. When rapport develops, trust develops. The presence of trust enables barriers to be taken down. This increases communications and allows for the therapist to get into the client's worldview. From here the therapist can "see what the client sees" opening up possibilities for change.

Therapeutic change allows the client change in:

1. viewing an event's perspective;
2. the disconnecting (deframing or reframing) of a particular from an array of other associations;
3. the freeing of a meaning from a frame to satisfy that meaning.

It is important that the human be seen as a system within a much larger system. In this view the part with the most flexibility in a system controls the system. This goes both for the internal or personal environment of the client as well as his/her external environment. The more choices that the client has in the environment the more chance there will be for the client to control the environment.

Psychotherapy is moving away from explanations, problems, and pathology. The direction is toward solutions, competence, and abilities. In order to do this the integration of the total personality is the desired objective. This integration is termed individuation. *Individuation is the awareness of, acceptance of, and action upon those dimensions of self that define an individual as unique and autonomous.* The implication is that the individual has:

1. an awareness of his/her own thoughts, feelings and behaviors;
2. an acceptance of these as valid representations of his/her self and as personal experience;
3. their identification seen as separate, internal experiences existing within the boundaries of self;
4. these thoughts, feelings and behaviors serving as the basis for making choices in the course of daily living.

The goal in promoting individuation is to help the client maximize the range of choices and consolidate their many aspects.

Self-actualization is another way of describing individuation. Self-actualization implies an inner-directed, efficient way of relating to ongoing experience. The client's expectations, values, beliefs, inner images, scripts and inner dialogues contribute to the self-concept and emanate from it. To aid in actualizing the self an "inner search" is necessary. This search can lead to more specific therapeutic changes.

There are certain values that facilitate individuation. These include the idea that:

1. Each person is unique. The problem is unique to that person. This does not mean that that person is the only one with that problem. This simply means that the way that the problem was acquired was unique. It was the client's own personal experience that brought the problem about.

2. Each person's experience is valid for him/her. No one can have another's experience. What happened to that person is theirs to own.

3. Each person relates to ongoing experience from his own frame of reference.

4. Join the client's frame of reference. In order to do this, rapport is of utmost importance. Without rapport you will be wasting both your client's and your own time.

5. The unconscious mind is rich in resources, is patterned from experience, and has positive capabilities. Tap into the unconscious by paying attention to the client. Reframe when necessary. Adjust the perspective constantly.

6. People make the best choice for themselves at any given moment. Everyone will choose what they think is the best for themselves. Choices tend to be based on self-interests and rarely involve the general environment. Increasing choice possibilities creates more choices that can involve the general environment.

7. Respect all messages from the client. Pay attention to what is said, and especially what is not said. More information comes through unconscious processes than through the conscious.

8. Teach choice; never attempt to take choice away.

9. The resources that the client needs lie within his own personal history. Reframing the resources that already exist can get your client to make different choices. Allowing the unconscious to use whatever resources exist already will create generative change. This generative change will affect the client's whole life.

10. The explanation, theory, or metaphor used to relate facts about a person is not the person: "The map is not the territory." In fact, the problem itself is most likely a metaphor. By using another metaphor to replace the one that is dysfunctional the client can operate with more effectiveness in his/her environment.

As a therapist it is well to keep these in mind. You are dealing with an individual, not simply a series of behaviors or a theoretical viewpoint. This will aid you in accomplishing the first purpose of the therapeutic intervention.

Techniques for change would best be directed toward the unconscious in order to bypass the conscious. The conscious mind is replete with biases, rigid patterns and limited experiences and learnings.The conscious mind concocts limiting beliefs. These beliefs stop us from searching for the resources we can use. This means that it is necessary to evoke and utilize the unconscious learnings of the client.

All of us have an active unconscious. It is able to direct thoughts and behaviors independently of the conscious processes. Consequently, in order to affect the deepest and longest lasting change it is more important to communicate with the unconscious than the conscious. The unconscious manifests itself in a great deal of simplicity and literalness. Interventions which stimulate the unconscious to search for the most efficient and effective solution would be indispensable. Communicating directly with the unconscious is the only way to tap into its unexplored potential.

In order to affect change it is necessary to be thinking about the future in a particular way. This has important effects on the future. Have your client construct a picture of how things will be when the problem is solved. Research has shown that people who imagine and explain success actually perform better than those who explain failure. Failure comes about from identifying with and focusing on the past. From this focus an individual assumes that because failure had occurred in the past it is inevitable that it will continue into the future. In order to overcome this past identification an approach using age-regression, doing and experiencing the present, and a pseudo-orientation in time or age-progression eliminates that fixation.

There are five stages for making change more effective. The *first* is to *change the status quo*. That is, change the automatic responses, the familiar behaviors, and the predictable ("I did it before and I'll do it again"). Once the status quo had been altered it becomes inevitable that other things will change as well. The *second* stage is to *introduce something different into the system.* A new way of thinking, a new perspective, a change of consciousness will all cause shifts that affect change. The *third* stage is to recognize that *confusion and chaos are evidence that the system is responding.* Confusion is nothing more than a step toward change. The greater the confusion, the greater the learning experience once the confusion has been resolved. The *fourth* stage is to *understand that change is a constant process.* It is subject to continuing awareness, to nurturing and practice. Most change tends to occur not in great leaps and bounds but in small steps. These small steps readjust the system a little at a time until the whole system is in harmony with the change, The *last* stage is to *set up a new status quo.* This means that you need to shift the energy direction. This can be done by any number of means: changing the self-image; buy a new wardrobe; find a new job; move to a new apartment; doing visual imagery of yourself without the problem; etc.

The first thing you need to do is to get the client to do is something—anything that is different from the usual complaint behaviors. Create an environment where these "new" behaviors are really normal and part of the client's regular repertoire. These new behaviors should have your client acting in self-respecting ways. Make sure that your client is associating the new behaviors with "good times." This will keep him/her focused on looking for the more positive aspects in life. You can assist this by giving the client an assignment to look for change and to report on it. What has the client noticed about the situation? Are these changes in the direction of the problem? Are they the kinds of change that are desired to be continued? Clients often notice something different between sessions. Often they will attribute the change to something other than the therapeutic session. Make sure that (s)he understands that change occurs after some specific alterations of thought have occurred.

It is necessary that the therapist is clear in his/her job as well (self rapport). Here are some questions for the therapist to become clear on with each client:

1. What do I have to offer this client to assist him in becoming well?
2. Do I have faith in his ability to grow?
3. Do I have ways to help him access his resources?
4. What perspective am I seeing this person from (i.e. specimen, treatment category, a person in trouble, good, bad, etc.)?

5. What can I do to assist this person's change?
6. Am I willing to be aware of myself enough to get out of his way?

If the client does not go along with the efforts of the therapist it is a message that the therapist has suggested changing in the wrong way. The person that needs to change in this instance is the therapist. What you need to do is to change and do something different. Be flexible. Your flexibility becomes a pattern for the client on the unconscious level and this behavior can help install change in the client. Needless to say, if you are communicating with the unconscious of your client you have a definite advantage. The unconscious will tell you what you need to do. You can also ask it what to do to assist change. It knows what is necessary.

Psychokinesiology has a huge advantage over any of the other types of therapy. It is *direct* communication with the unconscious of the client. It exists in a state of timelessness and going into the past and the future is quite easy. It takes orders precisely and any change in it is *generative*. Through Pk you are able to quickly, efficiently and elegantly get to the problem, realign resources and create generative change quickly and effectively. No other therapeutic tool has as much potential and can create as much life-affirming cognitive and behavioral change.

APPENDIX

BASIC PSYCHOKINESIOLOGY PROCEDURE

1. *Gaining Rapport*

   Information Gathering:

   a. "What's going on that you want to change?"

   b. Whatever the response, ask yourself, "What's the underlying problem?" Look for a fear, anxiety, helplessness, vulnerability, anger, guilt, or sadness.

   c. Ask yourself, "What purpose does this serve?" Ask your client, "What makes this a problem?"

   d. "What do you want to change?"

   e. "What has stopped you from changing until now?"

2. *Calibration Test*

   "When I say 'hold' I'm going to put a slight pressure on your arm. Resist the pressure. Hold."

3. *Polarity Test* (Optional)

   a. Place the index and middle fingers of either hand between the client's eyes and test the other arm. It should be weak

   b. Have the client place one hand on top of the head palm down and test. It should be strong. Turn the hand over and test. It should be weak. If the client is testing in reverse you will need to check it.

4. *Reaction Tests* (Optional)
   a. Name test: "Repeat. My name is (<u>real name</u>)." Test
                    "Repeat. My name is (<u>false name</u>)." Test
   b. Place test: "Repeat. I am in (<u>actual place</u>) now." Test
                    "Repeat. I am in (<u>false place</u>) now." Test
   c. Yes/No test: "Give me a 'yes.'" Test. "Give me a 'no.'" Test.

5. *Problem Statement Test*
   "Think about (<u>problem state</u>)." Test.

6. *Retrograde Polarity Test*
   "I want (<u>problem state</u>)." Test.
   "I don't want (<u>problem state</u>)." Test. Etc.

7. *Emotional Reflex Test*
   a. Test Organs
   b. Text Reflex Chart
   c. "Is this about a (<u>Fear, Anxiety, Helplessness, Vulnerability, Conflicting Motivations {approach/approach—approach/avoidance—avoidance/ avoidance}, Compromise, Silent Rules, Values, Dependencies, Boundaries {self or other's}, or Permission Seeking</u>.)?"
   d. "Is this (<u>emotion</u>) (<u>client's/another's</u>) emotion?"
   e. "If this is another's emotion, who's is it? Is it (<u>mother's, father's, etc.</u>)?"

8. *Original Time Test*
   "Yes or no, was there an original time for this problem?"

9. *Time Reversal Test*
   Tap the *Thymus Point* and say, "Think about (<u>problem state</u>) and go back to age ____. Was this problem present then?" Test. Etc.

10. *Resource Realigning*

    a. Client places hand on forehead palm down. "Yes or no, do we have enough information to clear this now?"

    b. "Yes or no, do we do this clearing with the eyes open?" Test.

    c. "Yes or no, do we do this clearing with the eyes closed?" Test.

    d. Do the Resource Realigning

11. *Problem Test*

    a. After the Resource Realigning test by stating, "Think about (problem state)." It should be weak.

    b. "Think about this healing." It should be strong.

12. *Healing Progression*

Tap the *Thymus Point* and state, "Think about this healing and go to age ____." Test. "Think about this healing and go to age ___." Test. Bring the healing up to the present.

13. *Time Progression*

After you have brought the healing up to the present, tap the *Thymus point* and state, "Take this healing up to tomorrow." Test. "Take this healing up to ___ years from now." Test. Etc.

14. *Return to the Present*

After you progressed the healing up years in the future, tap the *Thymus Point* to bring it back to the present.

15. *Ecology Check*

    a. "Yes or no, is there anything which is getting in the way of this change taking place?" and test. With a positive response go back and check if it is an emotion, a belief, a value, or an attitude. With an emotion check again: "Is this about a (Fear, Anxiety, Helplessness, Vulnerability, Conflicting Motivations {approach/approach—approach/avoidance—avoidance/avoidance}, Compromise, <u>Silent Rules, Values, Dependencies,</u> <u>Boundaries {self or other's}, or Permission Seeking.</u>)?"

"Is this (<u>emotion</u>) (<u>client's/another's</u>) emotion?"

"If this is another's emotion, who's is it? Is it (<u>mother's,</u> <u>father's, etc.</u>)?"

Then do a *Resource Realigning* or find the *Time of Origin.*

b. Check the *Retrograde Polarity* regarding the change.

c. Check the *Emotional Reflex Points*

Have your client think of the healing and test each of the *Emotional Reflex Points.*

Have your client think of the original problem and test the *Emotional Reflex Points.*

16. *Healing Statement*

Client put her hand on his forehead palm down and repeats. "This one is healed." Test. "There's more to do on that one." Test. "This one is healed." Test.

17. *Problem State Retest*

a. "Think about (<u>problem state</u>)." Test.

b. Retest the reflex point associated with that problem.

18. *Convincer*

a. Tap the *Thymus Point* and state, "It's __ hour before you got here. Think about (<u>problem state</u>)." Test. It will be strong.

b. Tap the *Thymus Point* and state, "Come back to the present. Think about (<u>problem state</u>)." Test. It will be weak.

CONSENT FOR NOVEL TREATMENT

The corrective technique that is intended to use is called *Psychokinesiology* (Pk). The theory behind this technique is that muscle testing can access unconscious processes, imbalances, and conflicting issues that may exist. This is a new technique and scientific studies to validate its potency are only now in the process of being performed. This technique involves both new concepts and limited physical touching. Before you undergo Pk it is important that you clearly understand what this technique is and that it is potentially controversial. Also, by signing this agreement you are consenting to the limited physical touching described in this consent form.

The theory behind Pk is that the body can respond to questions in a fashion that reveals information that is not coming from the conscious mind. The statements are phrased in a manner so that the muscle testing will indicate if there is complete agreement on the unconscious level. There will also be questions phrased in such a way as to indicate a "yes" or "no" response. The main muscle testing technique involves lying back down on a table with the arms outstretched and slightly back from a 90° angle. Statements can either be made strictly by the examiner alone or by the examiner with the client repeating. The test is made by the client resisting the examiner's movement while the examiner's hands are on the client's wrists. The test is to determine whether the muscle will lock, indicating a strong response, or release, indicating a weak response. Another method of testing may involve the examiner standing beside the client, holding the wrist and testing a single arm. It is also possible that the client's leg(s) may be used to test the response. If this is done then the examiner will test holding the client's ankles.

A further aspect of the limited touching involves tapping the *Thymus*

Point point. This *Thymus Point* is located in the center of the chest. Tapping this point, it is assumed, will send the unconscious mind to access specific time-related information.

The next step in the process is what is called a *Resource Realigning*. There are several methods for doing this. One method involves placing the palm of the hand on the client's forehead and tapping the top of the head. Another involves touching the client's temples with two fingers while the client is holding the breath. Another tap may be on the back at the number 8 thoracic vertebrae. There may also be instructions for the client to hold specific areas of the body. The theory behind the tapping is that it will dislodge any "energy" blockages which have been set up through an incongruence regarding the problem situation.

It is possible that there may be an experience of some memories from the past due to these procedures. At the present time there is substantial controversy in the mental health profession whether an emotional upset (referred to as a catharsis) is useful and whether the memory of past events actually assists in the emotional healing. More controversy exists over the validity of memories not consciously remembered. There is also dispute as to whether there are memories stored in some fashion by the body. One side of the debate asserts that what is uncovered in therapies are not in fact memories and are not literally true. Both sides of this debate do agree that care must be taken when memories appear. At this time it is best not to take them literally. They may be symbolic representations of the emotional problem.

Another area of dispute is over the difference between narrative and historical truth. This means that a memory may develop which is believed to be literally true. Upon research it is found that it is historically inaccurate. A number of therapists believe that what is important is not the historical accuracy of the memories, but the emotional validity to the client. In other words, something that is reported may not be historically accurate but may have tremendous validity to the client because it is a means of expressing something that cannot otherwise be expressed.

You, as the client, have the right to make decisions about what techniques are to be used with you. If you choose not to use this technique, that is your right. The risk of using this technique is twofold: 1) It may work in your particular case, or 2) You may come to believe that a memory that you recover is true when in fact it is not. The purpose of this process is to try to access matters which you cannot otherwise access. While it is believed that *Psychokinesiology* is a valid technique, it is new and there may be controversy concerning it. It is an ethical requirement to point out these issues to you so that you may make an informed decision whether you want to proceed.

You should understand that by signing this consent form you are agreeing to the limited physical contact as described herein.

I have carefully read this consent form and understand the nature of the treatment that is being provided and the fact that it is new. By signing below I agree to the treatment and to the limited physical contact as described above.

Dated:_____

Client's Signature

_____

Dated: _____

Examiner's Signature

_____

GLOSSARY

Abnormal Behavior – Behavior which is generally considered statistically unusual, strange or undesirable by most people, and a source of unhappiness for the individual and his/her family. A behavior which does not conform to the usual type of behavior expected.

Aggression – An attack or hostile action that can take different forms such as a physical or verbal assault, stubbornness or other forms of passive aggression, depression, or a verbal criticism.

Analogy – Making comparisons or drawing parallels. Reasoned as, the same as, similar to, or different than.

Anxiety – A general nervous system response that arouses the body to cope with a perceived or unknown danger. Anxiety can be cause by either a chemical or hormonal imbalance (clinical or endogenous anxiety) or an environmental situation (psychological or reactive anxiety).

Apoptosis – Cellular death. For example, infants are born with more neurons than they need. Cellular death occurs in order to "fine–tune" the brain and remove redundancy in cellular operations. As people age some neurons die off. By feeding with a fresh supply of nutrients, via the blood supply, it will insure their long life.

Apperception – Conscious perception; the act or process of perceiving. Apperception can be either directed, as attention, or undirected as fantasy or daydreaming.

Associative Learning – Learning caused by the union of two or more events.

Belief Networks – Models of the way one draws causal judgments about the world.

Calibration – The technique for determining the range or responding of a system or individual.

Cognitive Memory – Also called Representational Memory. The storage of copies or representations of learned activities.

Coherent Superposition – Two separate and distinct items which are spoken of as together and which affect each other such as the mind and body.

Consciousness – A subjective state of awareness of internal and external events. It involves attention, perception, learning, thinking, memory, and emotion. It has been described as a constantly changing continuum or stream shifting from object to object, from inside to outside and back again. It arises from the activity of the brain and is seen as a feedback loop between the thalamus deep inside of the brain and the cortex, the outer covering.

Constellations of Associations – Different pieces of information received by the nervous system and their perceived relationship affects one's behavior.

Contentually Dysfunctional – A lack of understanding of the meaning of a situation which does not follow the flow of thought or an incorrect conception of what is happening or being discussed bringing about an inappropriate choice or decision.

Context Dependent Learning – Learning which can be accessed only within the specific location in which it was learned.

Contextually Dysfunctional – A choice or decision which does not fit the conditions

Depression – A feeling of helplessness, hopelessness, inadequacy and extreme dejection, self–depreciation and self–abasement that affects one's living patterns (e.g. sleeping, eating, relationships). Depression can be caused by either a chemical or hormonal imbalance (clinical or endogenous depression) or an environmental situation (psychological or reactive depression).

Discontinuous – Without change or motion. Our perceptions are discontinuous. The brain puts the distinct perceptions together into a changing experience.

Ecology – The effects that the individual components of one part of the system have on the system at large. The effects that individual actions have on the individual and his experience. When something is ecologically sound it means that the whole system "agrees" on the change that one part has experienced.

Ego – The part of the personality which controls the identity–involved are emotional attachments to people, things, philosophies, groups, institutions, actions, and behaviors. All of one's "I ams."

Eidetic Memory – Photographic memory.

Emotion – A state where moods or feelings cause motivation toward or away from something. A complex set of physiological sensations combined with other thought processes (e.g. internal images and thoughts) to which meaning is attached.

Internal Sensations or Feelings – One's overall sensations at a particular moment in time.

Epiphenomena – After–effects. Thoughts are the after–effects of consciousness.

Emotional Reflex Points – Points on the body which correspond to specific internal organs and are associated with certain emotional responses.

Feedback – The continuous automatic return of data from a system for the purpose of making corrections.

Filters – The senses, attitudes, values, and other learned experiences which affect one's behavior.

Finite Causality – Also called Limited Causality. An event with a limited number of possible causes.

Generative Change – Change in one area affecting change in other areas.

Habit Learning – A type of non–cognitive learning which is not founded on knowledge and memories but on automatic connections between stimuli and responses.

Initial Phase of Memory Formation – The first of two phases of memory formation occurring in the hippocampus and later the neocortex of the brain.

Later Phase of Memory Formation – The second of two phases of memory formation which occurs in the reaction of the neurons themselves as the neurons learn to respond to more of an object's physical properties.

Long-Term Memory – The final level of memory which is relatively permanent memory.

Memory – The totality of all past experiences that can be remembered.

Neuron – Single nerve cell.

Neuronal Assembly – A set of neurons activated together and which are capable of changing depending on experience.

Nonassociative Learning – Learning resulting from experience without any connection being made to a specific event.

Normal Behavior – Behavior which agrees with or conforms to a society's accepted pattern of customs, rules, laws, fears, and taboos.

Observables – Actual objects; that which is perceived by the senses.

Peptide – A compound that contains two or more amino acids linked by a carboxyl group (carbon, oxygen, and hydrogen) of one amino acid and the amino group of another (nitrogen and hydrogen). Seen as the biochemical of emotion.

Polarized Static Effect – Noise in the "filters" that disrupts the harmonious flow of energy resulting in misdirected or miscommunicated energies.

Principle of Determinism – The principle which states that every natural even has a cause and that with research that cause can be found.

Rapport – The establishing of trust, harmony, and cooperation in a relationship. Meeting another in his/her model of the world. Matching or pacing another's behavior on different levels so as to enter into their experience.

Reality – All of the stimuli available for experience at a certain moment in time and point in space. The part of the universe which is not fantasized. That which is perceived by the physical senses.

Recomplexing – Behaviors associated with a particular complex of behaviors have either been changed and new ones added or strategically readjusted.

Resource – Any means that can be used to achieve an outcome (e.g. physiology, states, thoughts, strategies, experiences, people, events, or things).

Resource Realigning – In *Psychokinesiology* the technique for bringing internal resources in to support a client's changes. The process of eliminating blocked energies, thought patterns, and emotions for the purpose of creating more effective and efficient living experiences. Balancing hemispherical communications which can release more personal potential, emotional expression, eliminate fears, increase one's awareness of oneself and others, reduce anxiety and tension, and increase personal communications.

Retrograde Polarity – Energies not integrated into the system and traveling in reverse of the system which confront the forward moving energies. This causes energy blockages and imbalances. Retrograde Polarities create mental, emotional, physical, and spiritual imbalances.

Self–Rapport – Compatibility between one's internal and external feeling states and one's behavior.

Sensory Information Storage – The most basic level of memory where environmental stimulation is instantly and momentarily stored in the sensory system as a full representation. Subsequent environmental stimulation destroys part of the information as an experience continues.

Sequential Dysfunction – One's internal organization or order for decisions is organized in such a way that it gets in his/her way causing frustration and emotional problems.

Short–Term Memory – The second level of memory which consists of a set of things to which one is attending to a a given time. Its capacity is no more than 7 ± 2 items or chunks of data at a time.

Spatial Contiguity – Events occurring in space.

State Dependent Learning – Learning which can be accessed only within the specific state of mind in which it was originally installed.

Structure Mapping Theory of Analogy – Analogies that take into account causal and structural parallels between situations, as opposed to specific details. In General Semantics this is expressed as "The map is not the territory."

Synapse – Point of communications between one neuron and another.

Temporal Contiguity – Events occurring in time.

Temporally Dysfunctional – A behavior, belief, attitude, etc. which affects one's timing for making decisions and choices.

Time of Awareness – Point when an emotional or psychological problem is activated by an environmental circumstance.

Time of Origin – Point when an emotional or psychological problem actually began. The Time of Origin is usually out of awareness for it can be in utero or a genetic inheritance.

Time Progression Procedure – The *Psychokinesiology* process which takes the unconscious mind into the future.

Time Reversal Procedure – The *Psychokinesiology* process which takes the unconscious mind into the past.

BIBLIOGRAPHY

Baxter, L.R. et al, *Cerebral Metabolic Rates for Glucose in Mood Disorders*, **Archives of General Psychiatry**, 1985, 42, 441-447

Black, I.B. et al, *Neurotransmitter Plasticity at the Molecular Level*, **Science**, 21 Sept. 1984, 225, 4668, 1266-1270

Campbell, J. (Ed.) and Hull, R.F.C., **The Portable Jung**, Penguin Books, New York, NY, 1971

Cloninger, Robert C., *Neurogenetic Adaptive Mechanisms in Alcoholism*, **Science**, 24 Apr. 1987, 236, 4800, 410-416

Davidson, R.J., *Affect, Cognition, and Hemispheric Specialization*, **Emotions, Cognition, and Behavior,** 1984, Cambridge University Press, Cambridge, U.K., 320-365

Diamond, J., **Your Body Doesn't Lie**, Warner Books, New York, NY, 1979

Franklin, J., **Molecules of the Mind**, Atheneum, New York, NY, 1987

Gordon, Sol, **Psychology for You**, Oxford Book Co., New York, NY, 1974, 16-19

Greenfield, Susan A., **Journey to the Centers of the Mind**, W.H. Freeman & Co., New York, NY, 1995

Hsieh, C. & Phillips, R., *Reliability of Manual Muscle Testing with a Computerized Dynamometer*, **Journal of Manipulative Physiological Therapeutics**, 1990, 13, pp. 70-82

Hurley, Thomas J., III, *Beyond the Modern Worldview*, **Noetic Science Review**, Spring 1987, 2, 19-24

Kendall, H. et al, **Muscles: Function and Testing**, Williams & Wilkins, Baltimore, MD, 1983

Kracklaner, C., *Exploring the Life-World*, **Journal of Phenomenological Psychology**, Spr. 1972, 2, 2, 217-236

Langs, Robert, **Psychotherapy, A Basic Text**, Jason Aronson, New York, NY, 1982, 36-43

Leisman, G., Shambaugh, P. & Ferentz, A., *Somatosensory Evoked Potential Changes During Muscle Testing*, **International Journal of Neuroscience**, 1990, 45, pp. 143-151

Lenhart, R.E. and Katkin, E.S., *Psychophysical Evidence for Cerebral Laterality Effects in a High-Risk Sample of Students with Subsyndromal Bipolar Depressive Disorder*, **American Journal of Psychiatry**, 1986, 143, 602-607

LeShan, Lawrence, **The Medium, The Mystic, and The Physicist**, Ballantine Books, New York, NY, 1966

Love, Jeff, **The Quantum Gods**, Samuel Weiser, Inc., New York, N.Y. 1976

Marx, Jean L., *Proteins for all Seasons*, Research News, **Science**, 16 Aug. 1985, 229, 638-640

Netherton, M. and Shiffrin, N., **Past Lives Therapy**, Wm. Morrow and Co., Inc., New York, NY, 1978

Nichols, Michael and Paolino, Thomas, Jr. **Basic Techniques of Psychodynamic Psychotherapy**, Jason Aronson Inc., Northvale, NJ, 1986

Penrose, Roger, **Shadows of the Mind**, Oxford University Press, Oxford, UK, 1994

Pert, Candace, *Neuropeptides: The Emotions of Bodymind*, **Noetic Sciences Review**, Spr. 1987, 2, 13-18

_____, **Molecules of Emotion**, Scribner, New York, NY, 1997

Pines, Maya, *Suicide Signals*, **Science 83**, Oct. 1983, 55-58

Restak, Richard, **The Modular Brain**, Lisa Drew Books, New York, NY, 1994

Sapolsky, Robert M., *Stress in the Wild*, **Scientific American**, Jan. 1990, 262, 1, 116-123

Schacter, Daniel L., *Amnesia and Crime: How Much Do We Really Know?*, **American Psychologist**, 1986, 41, 286-295

Sheldrake, Rupert, *Rupert Sheldrake's Hidden Force*, **Science Digest**, Oct. 1981, 89, 9, 54-57

Smith, W.L., **Consulting the Body: Behavioral Kinesiology in Psychotherapy,** Pilgrimage, 1981

Talbot, Michael, **Mysticism and the New Physics**, Bantam Books, New York, NY, 1981

Tart, Charles, **States of Consciousness**, Psychological Processes, Incorporated, El Cerrito, CA, 1975

Tavris, Carol, *Coping With Anxiety*, **Science Digest**, Feb. 1986, 46-51, 80-81

Verney, Thomas, M.D. & Kelly, John, **The Secret Life of the Unborn Child**, Dell Publishing, New York, NY, 1981

Wadsworth, C., et al, *Intrarater Reliability of Manual Muscle Testing and Hand-Held Dynamometry*, **Physical Therapeutics**, 1987, 67, pp. 1342-1347

Webb, D, Jr. & Fagan, J., *The Impact of Dream Interpretation Using Psychological Kinesiology on the Frequency of Recurring Dreams*, **Journal of Psychotherapy and Psychosomatics**, 1993, 59, pp. 203-208

Wolf, Fred A., **Taking the Quantum Leap**, Harper and Row, Publishers, San Francisco, CA., 1981

Wolman, Benjamin B., **Dictionary of Behavioral Science**, Van Nostrand Reinhold Co., New York, NY, 1973

Zukav, Gary, **The Dancing Wu Li Masters**, Bantam Books, New York, NY, 1979

Zeig, Jeffrey K. and Lankton, Stephen R., **Developing Ericksonian Therapy**, Brunner/ Mazel Publishers, New York, NY, 1988

APPLIED KINESIOLOGY CERTIFICATIONS

Emotional Complex Clearing 6151 Del Cerro Blvd. San Diego, CA 92120
Brad May, Ph.D., M.F.C.C. Developer

NeuroLink 2000 P.O. Box 25506 St. Heliers, Auckland, New Zealand
Allan K. Phillips, D.C. Developer

Total Body Modification 1907 East Foxmore Ci. Sandy, UT 84092
Victor Frank, D.C. Developer

B.E.S.T. Morter Healthcare 1000 W. Poplar, Rogers, AK 72756
Dr. Morter, Jr., B.S.M.A.D.C. Developer

CONTACT INFORMATION:

P.O. Box 371814
Reseda, CA 91337

email: roberly@aol.com

ALEXANDER S. HOLUB, Ph.D.

Alexander S. Holub has been teaching Psychology in the Los Angeles Community College District for 25 years. He holds a Doctoral Degree in Psychology. He is a member of the American Association for the Advancement of Science and the Institute of Noetic Sciences. Dr. Holub has certification in Rational-Emotive Behavioral Therapy being taught by its founder Dr. Albert Ellis. He has further certifications in Neuro-Linguistic Programming where he holds Practitioner, Master Practitioner and Trainer certifications. For five years he had been a facilitator for a S.M.A.R.T. (Self-Management and Recovery Training) Recovery group. S.M.A.R.T. Recovery is an alternative to the 12-step approach based on the work of Dr. Albert Ellis and cognitive therapy. Dr. Holub has been a practicing hypnotherapist for more than 25 years. He has Applied Kinesiology certification in Total Body Modification (TBM), Emotional Complex Clearing (ECC), and NeuroLink 2000. Along with his partner, Evelyn Budd-Michaels, Ph.D., he has been pioneering in the use of Applied Kinesiology in counseling and therapy. They have presented their findings at many conferences in the western United States. Among the conferences were: the *Western States NLP Conference* in Park City, UT; the *American Board of Hypnotherapy* in Irvine, CA; the *Whole Life Expo* in Los Angeles, CA; and *1995 NLP Comprehensive International Conference* in Denver, CO. He has written articles for: *Anchor Point Journal of Borderland Sciences*, *Psychic Reporter*, and *The Journal of Educational and Psychological Measurements*. He has studied Southern Shao-Lin kung-fu from the renowned late Grandmaster Wong, Ark-Yuey and has written articles on kung-fu for *Martial Arts Masters, Black Belt, Karate/Kung Fu Illustrated*, and *Inside Kung Fu* magazines. Dr. Holub's interests are wide and varied ranging from Theoretical Physics, Cosmology, Mystical Traditions and Mysticism, Mythology, and Art, to Ancient History, Archeology, Anthropology Paleontology, and Human behavior.

EVELYN BUDD-MICHAELS Ph.D.

For most of her life Dr. Evelyn Budd-Michaels has searched for solutions that would allow us to live healthier, happier, and more prosperous lives. She has discovered many principles and techniques which help to accomplish these goals and allow her to draw upon a variety of methods while working with her clients.

Dr. Evelyn Budd-Michaels has a Ph.D. in Psychology from Summit University and is certified as a Practitioner, Master Practitioner, and Trainer in Neuro-Linguistic Programming (NLP). Her training in kinesiology techniques include Total Body Modification (TBM), Holistic Energy Restructuring, Bio-Energetic Synchronization Technique (BEST), Emotional Complex Clearing (ECC), Neuro-Emotional Technique (NET) and development techniques. Dr. Budd-Michaels is a certified member of the American Board of Hypnotherapy. She is also a renowned expert on handwriting Analysis. Her expertise in this field allows her to use handwriting as another diagnostic tool to assist her clients.

Dr. Evelyn Budd-Michaels is a counselor with over 25 years experience in assisting people with personal growth and development. She has reached millions of people throughout the world through TV, radio, and seminars. She also produced and was the hostess of her cable television show *Synergy 4 Success.* This talk show presented new and unique information to assist viewers to achieve personal and professional success. Guests included world champions, artists, celebrities, and interesting people from many walks of life. Articles she has written, including Stress Reduction, Creating Happier Relationships with Yourself and Others, Secrets Revealed in Your Handwriting, Communication, and Walking the Spiritual Path have been published in magazines and journals. Dr. Budd-Michaels and Dr. Holub are currently working on their next book titled: *How to Get What You Want in Your Life.* It is scheduled for publication in 2000.

What People are Saying About the Psychokinesiology Process

"Dr. Holub's remarkable treatise is almost more than one can anticipate in a single volume or in one reading due to its broad coverage. It is especially timely in the movement towards the mind-body approach in the therapeutic process — as compared with the usual talk therapy.

Psychokinesiology contains significant insights into the understanding of human behavior. It can be a valuable addition to any library. Beyond that, it is highly worthwhile to be involved in at least one session to discover the seemingly entrancing response as a result — even in a single session.

I believe this innovative material is specially appropriate for students, practitioners, and laypersons alike. It will certainly open up an appreciation for the extent and breadth of its therapeutic concepts and practices."

V.V. DiMeo, Ph.D.
Psychologist (Ret.)

"This is like a guarantee of certainty. This has a profound effect. I have no hesitancy talking about it. It's possible to achieve some miraculous changes."

Gary Boone, M.A., MFCC
NLP Master Trainer

"Of all of the therapy, this is the most liberating experience I've ever had. I feel free from those darker emotions that were holding me back."

Katrina W., Ph.D.
Psychotherapist

"I have a different viewpoint about money. Within the first week unexpected opportunities came to me and my client load has increased so that I have more clients than I can handle."

Nancy M., Attorney

"Since being cleared I am able to perform and audition without feeling any nervousness or anxiety. This freedom allows me to put my total focus on the performance and stay in the 'now.' It has made me a better actor."

Michael G., Actor

"I am truly impressed by the depth and scope of *Psychokinesiology.* The works delves into the detailed methods of how we truly think. It is not an easy read or meant for the casual enthusiast. Rather, this work is a scientific-based writing that is based on real clinical evidence regarding the human thinking and conscious process. It is focused towards those who are currently in practice and wish to deepen their skills and effectiveness. Also, it provides reasoning for clinical phenomena that goes beyond an explanation of "it just works."

Psychokinesiology uses proven methods of neuropsychological intervention and enhances clinical methodology to bring the practitioner solid and satisfying results. It borrows from some of the most current and exciting methodology to dealing with human neuro-psycho-emotional function. As a practitioner of Neuro Emotional Technique (NET), Neurolink, Total Body Modification (TBM), and Applied Kinesiology (AK), I am impressed with the system of Psychokinesiology as it blends this proven system of care together in a manner that really works on a deep and lasting level. It gives the practitioner a model and systemic approach to mastering the linguistics and thought process of the brain. This seems to be the key to entering the brain. The correct phrasing is just as important, if not more, than simply "fixing" the thought process. This work expands my clinical abilities for dealing with the awesome complexities of my patients.

Any practitioner dealing with the emotional side of the health triangle (bio-chemical/emotional/physical) needs to have this manuscript in their library so they can truly understand how the thinking, emotional, and surviving human functions as a homeostatic unit. Once read and understood, the practitioner's scope is enhanced. Thus, they are able to serve at a deeper level the needs of their patients and loved ones.

Importantly, it is a system that is efficient and well thought out. I will be using this system in my practice. I recommend that my fellow practitioners consider adding this technique to their practice as it goes beyond the many techniques those in alternative health care have been provided. *Psychokinesiology* gets to the point and provides a solid method to help the practitioner become more efficient and achieve a higher level of clinical excellence."

Randall W. Robirds, D.C., Chiropractic Physician
Applied Health Dynamics

To Order Other Titles
Call
800-729-4131